14

THE LOTTERY OF LIFE

THE LOTTERY OF LIFE

THE NEW GENETICS AND THE FUTURE OF MANKIND

PHILIPPE FROSSARD

BANTAM PRESS

LONDON · NEW YORK · TORONTO · SYDNEY · AUCKLAND

TRANSWORLD PUBLISHERS LTD
61–63 Uxbridge Road, London W5 5SA

TRANSWORLD PUBLISHERS (AUSTRALIA) PTY LTD
15–23 Helles Avenue, Moorebank, NSW 2170

TRANSWORLD PUBLISHERS (NZ) LTD
Cnr Moselle and Waipareira Aves,
Henderson, Auckland

Published 1991 by Bantam Press
a division of Transworld Publishers Ltd
Copyright Dr Philippe Frossard 1991

A catalogue record for this book is
available from the British Library.

ISBN 0593 024664

Typeset in 11 on 12pt Sabon by
Falcon Typographic Art Ltd, Edinburgh and London.
Printed in Great Britain by
Mackays of Chatham, PLC, Chatham, Kent.

To my sister Christine

CONTENTS _____

ACKNOWLEDGEMENTS ────────────

This book is a tribute to the countless number of scientists who, by their continuous and creative efforts, lead the world of scientific and medical research. I am aware that many of them might wonder why their names have been left out in discussions of their discoveries. The reason is that my aim has been to provide an overview of the promises kept by molecular biology, not to give encyclopedia-like entries for each scientist and each discovery made. I hope they will understand.

I am particularly indebted to Professor Serge N. Vinogradov (Ann Arbor, Michigan), for his advice and comments which have contributed to improve this book.

Jeffrey Simmons (London) agreed at the start of this project to represent me as a literary agent. His professional experience and sense of ethics have constituted an invaluable source of inspiration for me.

I wish to thank Mark Barty-King from Bantam Press for his confidence in me, and Georgina Morley for her patience during the last stages of preparation of the book.

Foreword on Molecular Biology and Plan of the Book

MOLECULAR BIOLOGY IS A NEW FIELD. IT STARTED ITS EXPLOSIVE RISE only about fifteen years ago, after scientists had refined the methods of manipulation of hereditary material.

When I was a student in the early 1970s, molecular biology was a general term designating several disciplines that were not always clearly related. For me it was a branch of biochemistry and biophysics concerned with the properties and function of all kinds of large molecules – the macromolecules – such as proteins, polysaccharides and deoxyribonucleic acid (DNA). I was particularly interested in the structure of a very large protein, the haemoglobin of *Eisenia fetida*, a worm living in organic composts. It fascinated me that some 150 or so individual protein chains aggregate to form a very large haemoglobin molecule responsible for transporting oxygen to the various body parts of the animal, while in humans the haemoglobin molecule is composed of only four individual protein chains. That was the sort of molecular biology I was working on in those days.

After completing my formal university training in 1979 I realized that in order to remain a molecular biologist I would have to switch to the new and totally different field of – same name! – molecular biology, which by then had come to designate the branch of science exclusively involved in unravelling the mysteries of the DNA molecule, the genetic material of all living organisms. Of course, the desire to be called a molecular biologist was not what prompted me to take up DNA research. Times had changed and new techniques were available. It was obvious that the new molecular biology was about to trigger a revolution in both basic and applied medical research.

I decided to spend a year in Pierre Chambon's laboratory (at the Louis Pasteur Medical Centre, the University of Strasbourg), and there I learned these new experimental methods as part of

Jean-Louis Mandel's research team, which was then laying the foundations of what was to become molecular genetics. Afterwards I moved to America and completed a post-doctoral fellowship in the Department of Human Genetics at the University of Michigan Medical Center. There, while I was working on the genetic abnormalities that cause diseases such as sickle cell anaemia (a common form of hereditary anaemia among blacks and Mediterraneans) and Lesch-Nyhan syndrome, I realized the full extent of what molecular biology could do in terms of the diagnosis, treatment and cure of human disease.

At that time, in the early 1980s, biotechnology companies were mushrooming. With them came the novelty of being able to carry out university-type research with readily available funds – a seductive prospect for someone wanting to do applied research in scientific fields where experiments are costly. I joined the team of California Biotechnology, Inc., located in Mountain View, California, in the heart of Silicon Valley, when the company was just starting its operations. The scientific projects that I conducted there concentrated on applying the methods of molecular biology and human genetics to disorders with a hereditary component.

A Field by Any Other Name . . .

Molecular biology incorporates the methods of several previously distinct disciplines, including biochemistry, pharmacology, medicine, physiology, bacteriology, virology and cell biology. As such, it contributes to the blurring of the boundaries between these different fields, all of which have accepted its techniques to a certain extent. It constitutes a mixture of techniques and methods rather than a separate discipline.

The aim of molecular biology is to discover the mysteries hidden in genetic (or hereditary) material and the new experimental techniques which have allowed it to grow so explosively are referred to as recombinant DNA technology and genetic engineering. However, there are no clear-cut definitions and molecular biology, recombinant DNA technology and genetic engineering tend to be used as interchangeable labels in all the laboratories I have been to.

Biotechnology is another frequently heard word. It refers to the application of the techniques of molecular biology to obtain new products for use in medicine, agriculture and other industries. Since the advent of molecular biology, the business community has realized how much it can benefit from the new techniques of gene cloning and genetic diagnoses, as well as tests based on the use of monoclonal antibodies. All the major traditional pharmaceutical and chemical companies have started or are planning to start biotechnology divisions as part of their research programmes.

Molecular genetics is a discipline concerned with the investigation of hereditary diseases at the DNA level. Molecular genetics combines the newest recombinant DNA techniques with classical genetics and uses notions borrowed from epidemiology, statistics and mathematical modelling. My field of expertise has become the molecular genetics of multifactorial disorders, and in this book I describe some of the medical applications of this discipline.

I have tried to be very selective and to confine the discussion to the subject that has particularly interested me over the past twelve years: the new genetics and its implications for the future of mankind. The tools we have forged will help us to explore the secrets hidden in the hereditary material of all living organisms. Yet our quest will not always follow a smooth path, and we will need to face up to the repercussions of our discoveries, even the darkest ones.

I must admit at this point that the general picture shown here attempts to reflect the current status of research throughout the world. That picture has, however, been drawn by someone living and working in America and, therefore, the pencil strokes inevitably evoke an American setting.

The Limits of What We Can Do

Although the emphasis in this book is on general principles of molecular genetics as they help us to probe life's unknown mechanisms, from time to time I will mention certain projects that are still in their preliminary research phases and have yet to provide definitive conclusions. It is an enlightening process to follow an idea from the time of its conception, through the initial series of experiments, which indicate whether or not the project should continue and what direction it should take, to the appearance of the first set of results.

I see no point in cataloguing what has been done in the recent past and what will probably be done in the near future; the facts would be out of date by the time they were published. Rather, I wish to outline the general principles that are beginning to emerge from molecular biologists' investigations, the principles that are fundamental to our understanding of the processes governing life, when life is reduced to a collection of molecular mechanisms.

We know, however, that a purely reductive approach cannot

explain the essence of life, even though there is little empirical evidence for the existence of a life force. Here some modern scientists feel the need for a more classical approach, seeking dialogue with philosophers, because the jump from biochemical reactions to the manifestations of life itself involves such a large unknown. Keeping in mind what we have learned, what we can reasonably attain and what will always remain alien to pure scientific investigation is a recurrent preoccupation of this book.

How the Book Is Structured

The Introductory chapter examines how far down the road we have already gone, how far we can go and whether there are limits to what we can do. Just what are scientists up to?

I have then divided the book into three parts, arranging material in a logical order. I believe, however, that each part and even each chapter can be read independently.

Part One shows what we have learned about human genetic material, how scientists proceed in its exploration and how the most recent discoveries are applied in day-to-day medical practice.

The essence of the knowledge we seek to acquire is rooted in the genetic make-up of individuals, and our ultimate goal is to discover all the secrets hidden in the DNA molecule – the physical backbone of our genetic blueprint. Chapter 1 outlines our current understanding of the DNA molecule. Chapter 2 explores the world of gene splicers, describing some of the tools we have forged to manipulate DNA and considering the effects of these new methods on various fields of medicine. The object of this chapter is also to look at what can be done to fight disease: the tools forged by molecular biologists have led to the cloning of genes and a possible practical application of gene cloning for patients is the designing and production of new-generation recombinant DNA drugs. How are these made? Why are they more appropriate and more effective than traditional medications? Why are they also more expensive? Recombinant DNA products are ideal for treating severe and fatal hereditary illnesses. Gene therapy, on the other hand, gives humanity the prospect of curing these illnesses. The aim of this method is to replace disease-causing genes with their healthy counterparts. Is this technique really feasible and are we ready for it?

Unravelling the structure of the DNA molecule has contributed to the identification of variations between individual genetic materials. These variations are used as genetic markers (Chapter 3). Obtaining a complete sequence of the constituents of the human genome would permit the discovery of all genetic markers and all the approximately 100,000 genes contained within a human DNA molecule. This is precisely the aim of the human-genome-sequencing programme, which has been controversial even among scientists (Chapter 4). The applications of gene-marker technology include the development of methods for paternity testing and criminal and forensic examinations (Chapter 5), and also of diagnostic tests for hereditary diseases (Chapter 6).

Part Two looks at what we are learning about several devastating illnesses which are a major concern to the Western world. Our understanding of most of them is based on a concept expressed by the word 'multifactorial', meaning that the progression of these diseases results from the interplay between many unrelated factors that are both genetic and environmental.

In order to show the significance of molecular genetic studies and their contribution to the practice of medicine, to define the concept of genetic predisposition, to illustrate how far scientists have gone and where the boundaries of their knowledge lie, to present some moral issues associated with the implications of new genetics and also to describe the direction of current research, I decided to start with the representative example of cardiovascular disease, or disease of the heart and vessels. Chapter 7 focuses specifically on the major risk factors associated with atherosclerosis, a cardiovascular disease in which hardening of the arteries occurs due to cholesterol deposition.

Three separate reasons motivated my choice. First, cardiovascular disease is the archetypal multifactorial disease. Second, its incidence is very high: in the Western world, one person out of two dies from the complications of cardiovascular disease. And third, research in this area using the methods of molecular genetics has been one of my specialties for the past eight years. Naturally, the principles governing the development of atherosclerosis also apply to other challenging disorders and symptoms associated with cardiovascular disease: namely, hypertension, diabetes and obesity. Identification of the processes involved in all of these clinical entities reminds us how much they interact with each other and how arbitrary is our classification.

There are other so-called 'modern' diseases whose underlying mechanisms are complex but for which biotechnology is bringing hopes for both early diagnosis and treatment. Among these we have started to decipher the puzzle of cancer (Chapter 8), allergies (Chapter 9) and neuro-psychiatric diseases, three of which – Alzheimer's disease, schizophrenia and major affective disorders (depression and manic depression) – are analysed in more detail in Chapters 10, 11 and 12.

Part Three is devoted to a discussion of general issues stemming from the applications of molecular biology.

Society is slowly getting away from traditional medicine, which is concerned with the treatment of peripheral manifestations of disease, and has entered an era of preventive medicine, where the combination of early detection through diagnosis of genetic susceptibility and implementation of preventive measures decreases the individual's likelihood of being affected by debilitating diseases. For society's benefit, the cost of targeted prevention is cheaper than the cost of treatment. Meanwhile, the individual's gain is on two fronts: increased life span and improved quality of life (Chapter 13).

Unravelling disease mechanisms leads us to the heart of a central question: is heredity or the environment responsible? Today the old debate of Nature *vs* Nurture has become obsolete: both the hereditary blueprint and environmental factors play a role in the development of a disease. The interaction between these two components is also at the base of the reactions underlying human character, human behaviour and intelligence (Chapter 14). With this conceptual approach, we understand why diseases are so prevalent. We are also beginning to comprehend the complex organization of living organisms (Chapter 15).

Molecular biology applied to industry is placed under the general label of 'biotechnology'. Because it represents a rapidly expanding technology and a key investment for the future, biotechnology constitutes a promise not only for improving human health but also for the economy of industrialized countries. The success of biotechnology companies, spanning a mere fifteen-year period, has given new meaning to the concept of venture capital. Where is biotechnology heading today and what can we reasonably expect from it (Chapter 16)?

Considerations of profit-sharing and the future of biotechnology companies may seem to be only distantly related to the original expectations raised by the techniques of molecular biology – promises for a better future while keeping the individual's interests in mind. Worries about making money out of human disease generate additional ethical and moral questions. They also raise more pragmatic issues. Who will reimburse the high cost of preventive treatments and of genetic-screening tests? What will be the attitude of insurance companies? To what extent can we introduce legislation to govern the questions raised by new genetics? We need to answer these questions urgently, and it is everyone's duty to participate in the processes of decision-making and in the elaboration of satisfactory guidelines (Chapter 17).

INTRODUCTION _____

How Far Can We Go?

1933. NAZI GERMANY STERILIZES 56,000 INDIVIDUALS WITH 'HEREDITARY' defects.

1978. Birth of Louise Brown, first 'test tube' baby.
First genetic test for diagnosis of sickle cell anaemia.

1982. Scientists create 'super-mice'. These mice grow much bigger than ordinary ones because of the introduction into their hereditary material of rat genetic material which manufactures growth hormone.
Human insulin produced by recombinant DNA techniques for the treatment of diabetes.

1983. Public statement of the Singapore Plan by Prime Minister Lee Kuan Yew. The government decides to give incentives to couples with higher IQs to procreate, while discouraging couples with lower IQs and in lower socio-economic groups from having children.
Gene responsible for Huntington's disease localized in the human genetic material.

1987. One gene implicated in Alzheimer's disease pinpointed.
Cystic fibrosis gene localized.

1989. Cystic fibrosis gene identified.
Abnormal gene causing Duchenne's myopathy characterized.

1990. England. Birth of Daniele and Nathalie Edwards, whose sex had been selected after determination in a test tube (in that family, boys would have 50 per cent odds of being affected by a terrible, hereditary, neurological disease called leucodystrophy of the adrenals).

India and People's Republic of China. The governments take the decision to control population growth with a policy of one child per family. It soon becomes obvious that a 'good' baby is a boy. Indeed, traditionally the son takes care of his family, and in particular of the elder, while a daughter will go and live with her husband's family. Baby girls are therefore drowned at birth and are then considered stillborn. By 1980 government officials from the People's Republic of China were imposing strict enforcement of the 'one family one child' law and by 1981 statistics effectively proved that a higher number of boys were born.

'What are you scientists up to?' 'Is genetic manipulation safe?' 'Are there any frontiers to what we can do?' 'How far can you go?' These are the questions that non-scientists have most frequently asked me over the past ten years upon hearing that I am a molecular geneticist. They suggest that the public at large wants information about recent discoveries in the field of biomedical research in order to make its own judgement.

Many medical questions arouse great interest. For example, why is heart disease so prevalent in the Western world? Why is its toll rising so rapidly in developing countries? Can we detect an individual's genetic susceptibility to atherosclerosis or to hypertension, and if so, can we do something to prevent it developing in the individual concerned? What are the relative contributions of environmental and genetic factors to the development of these diseases? Will we be able to cure them?

Along the same lines of thought, are cancer and mental illnesses inherited? If it can be shown that they do indeed have a genetic basis, can we seek to eliminate them by gene therapy, replacing the defective genetic material with its healthy counterpart in a patient's DNA? Today many laboratories are actively working on developing efficient methods of gene therapy. Should we impose limits on these experiments? If not, don't we run the risk of going towards a new form of eugenics?[*1]

In theory the idea of selecting for specific traits could be carried to extremes which are frightening to imagine. Certain people, some of them scientists, have advocated their choices for selections based on traits such as good looks, intelligence or both. Hence the idea of running a sperm bank whose donors are Nobel Prize recipients, or the Singapore Plan, which is only one among many current examples.

[1*] Eugenics, a science defined and developed by the British traveller and physiologist Sir Francis Galton in 1883, is the study of the conditions most favourable for human reproduction in order to improve the human race. Although this may at first sound innocuous, the concept of eugenics has been perverted by various groups seeking both justification for their theories of the existence of a 'super race' and the ways to attain it. The misuse of eugenics reached a peak in Nazi Germany, where horrific medical experiments were carried out on people not members of the ruling Aryan élite.

It is not surprising that people have their own opinions about what society should be like. Unfortunately, the line between knowing what is fantasy and what is a possible reality is sometimes very thin. History has shown how certain political leaders can make crowds follow them and carry out their ideas. Consciously or unconsciously, we all have in mind the fear of witnessing history's darkest pages repeat themselves.

Everyone possesses physical or mental traits which could be advocated as a model for selection. With the next generation of molecular-biology techniques, unscrupulous leaders might not even need to bend an individual's mind to make a given ideology acceptable. Let us, for an instant, leave the present and enter the world of fiction. We can easily extrapolate from what we know today and write a possible future scenario. Let us imagine that we know all the genes contained in human DNA and that we have the capability to manipulate them *in vivo*.*[1] It would then be possible to modify an egg's DNA in order to engineer a human being whose appearance and behaviour matched one's idea of perfection (of course, the very idea of perfection is itself a variable, depending on the frame of reference arbitrarily chosen). Desirable traits would thus be hard-wired into the original egg before it started to divide and begin the nine-month process resulting in a human being bearing all the desired traits.

At present this scenario belongs to the world of science fiction. We are still a long way from knowing all the human genes and from mastering the techniques required to replace a single gene, let alone to engineer a cell's complete DNA! That would also imply manipulating the DNA from germ lines (the cells that are passed from generation to generation). Today there is a ban on such experiments. Only somatic-cell (cells that are not passed on to the offspring) manipulations are allowed. In any case, technically we are not able genetically to engineer super-humans, zombies or monsters. However, we can easily detect the sex of an embryo starting from the sixth week of gestation, and we know that the results of such tests have been used to terminate pregnancies of unwanted sexes (does it come as a surprise to hear that over 98 per cent of the terminations were decided upon after learning that the embryo was female?). Legislation dealing with this subject is being considered in many countries.

[1]* *in vivo* means 'within a living organism'. The phrase is used often in science, as is its opposite, *in vitro*, 'in the laboratory or in an artificial environment: i.e., outside the living organism' (literally: 'in glass').

The White Horse Episode

During the time that I have spent visiting research teams with which we were pursuing scientific collaborations, I also met with many non-scientists, and I have had many opportunities to become aware of the extent of their curiosity in the many recent medical and scientific advances. A recent episode, which stands out among all these occasions, took place in an Alsatian restaurant called 'Le Cheval Blanc'.

In that part of Alsace, local people who have suffered heart attacks formed an association optimistically called the Club of Former Coronary Patients. They meet once a week at a local swimming pool, where they exercise to improve their physical fitness and thereby reduce the risk of another heart attack. (I should add as an aside that we all tend to have a rather ambivalent attitude towards the prevention of disease and the fight for life, feeling that after a burst of healthy exercise we deserve to indulge ourselves.) After their swimming sessions, the members of the Club of Former Coronary Patients proceed to the local restaurant and enjoy generous portions of rich Alsatian cooking, accompanied by some splendid local wines.

On this particular occasion the chef-owner (himself a heart attack survivor) introduced me after dinner to two club members and we soon started chatting about recent advances in the treatment of heart disease. At this point the waitress, whose mother is affected by severe atherosclerosis, promptly joined in. While we were sipping Alsatian raspberry brandy, one of the waiters fetched a paper tablecloth, which became an improvised canvas. With the help of sketches of the human heart, obstructed arteries, DNA molecules and genetic markers, we carried on our discussion for two hours.

The people I talked with that evening did not deny their illness and they were eager to hear about the real risks. Naturally, they wanted to understand the true value – as far as we know it – of preventive measures, such as adopting a 'healthier' life style and using cholesterol-lowering drugs. Two observations struck me. The first was their desire to be informed about the current state of medical research, in which molecular biology has played a major role over the past few years. The second was the fact that, despite their will to learn about heart disease, a subject that touched them personally, they were almost totally ignorant of its nature.

The general public might understand very little of what has been happening recently in the field of medicine, but everyone is aware of the great attention paid to major new discoveries, because their repercussions will inevitably change society's attitude towards disease and human behaviour. We all guess that molecular biology participates in the battle against disease. Indeed, the development of more appropriate and more efficient drugs opens new horizons for both treatment and prevention. Long-term consequences for the individual include increased life expectancy, decreased infantile mortality and a reduction of the number of serious illnesses; for society they raise the prospect of a drastic decrease in the cost of health care.

Molecular biology creates new openings for investment, and the success of biotechnology companies influences the economy of diverse fields, including medicine, the pharmaceutical industry, agriculture, the manufacture of laboratory instruments and the whole area of reagents and products for both research and clinical laboratories. It allows us to ask that most fundamental of questions: 'What is life?'

Of course, molecular biology is not the only way forward. Understanding disease, alleviating human suffering and increasing both the length and the quality of life have always been the main preoccupations of science and medicine, but the exploration of these themes has been enormously facilitated by the new tools that we have developed.

Good and Evil

We humans have the ability to integrate our emotions with an extraordinary power to analyse, rationalize and conceptualize the phenomena that we observe. When we hear the noise made by a tree crashing to the forest floor, we might ask ourselves whether these noises actually exist or are real only in our minds, because we happen to be there to hear them with our sense of hearing, which is intricately associated with brain function. Do events really take place as we believe them to do?

The creation of the earth, 4.5 billion years ago, triggered a series of dynamic processes that led, little by little, to the appearance of the first organized life forms, 3.5 billion years ago. Under the pressure of evolution, these primitive life forms slowly developed into the many plants and animals that have populated the earth. Some of them are now extinct, though they can be observed as fossils, and others are still living today. At the top of the evolutionary pyramid stand human beings, inheritors of the most elaborate, sophisticated thought processes. These give us the power to claim that the existence of life is the result of complex interactions between heredity and environment.

All manifestations of life have their origins in the multitude of biochemical reactions characteristic of living organisms. With the tools we have forged, we are starting to comprehend the biochemical basis of diseases, behaviour, learning, memory, alcoholism, drug addiction, compulsion to gamble, passions and pleasure. However, no simple deterministic vision of the universe can explain the qualitative jump from the mineral world of rocks and water to the world of living species, or from lower animal species to humans. The greatest scientific challenge that we are facing is twofold: we are seeking, first, a definition of the 'life force' that underlies existence; and second, the wisdom to understand human thought processes.

Today's scientific views strive to integrate individual, restricted discoveries into universal theories, and to put advances in their proper place within the more general framework of a cosmic blueprint. Molecular biologists and molecular geneticists focus their energy on deciphering the complexity of the genetic material of living species. Molecular biology and genetics, however, are more than theoretical disciplines concerned with interesting intellectual exercises. They offer direct applications for our day-to-day life, for the practice of medicine and for our perception of disease and behaviour.

We should handle the reproduction revolution as we would handle a ticking bomb. The convergence of *in vitro* fertilization and genetic manipulation unveils a future where we will be able to modify embryos at will, conferring desired characteristics to the embryos and thereby manufacturing babies '*à la carte*' – a bothersome Huxleyian scheme that awakens deep emotional issues. Forthcoming interrogations about individual identity and transmission of heredity will echo society's questions about the role and value of men and women. If we follow the growing trend for the blending of cultural values worldwide, we run the risk of being tempted by genetic uniformity, thus erasing the legacy of genetic diversity.

Tailoring certain characteristics of living organisms to specific needs is nothing new. Traditional breeding techniques have long been used to ameliorate bacteria, plants and animals: roses, pigeons, dogs and cats are living proofs. The techniques used took time to develop. The methods for splicing and piecing together genetic material, however, provide mankind with the means of conferring desirable traits at an unprecedented speed.

We are cautious with and fear the applications of molecular genetics. We know the positive aspects: recombinant DNA drugs, diagnoses for genetic diseases and diagnoses for predisposition to certain diseases, such as heart disease and cancers. One day we will also be able to determine genetic predispositions to skills and talents.

At the same time, though, we are justifiably afraid of possible abuses
– which brings us back to the field of social ethics.

Bigger Rats Are Easier to Shoot

Despite wide, growing interest, the general public often has a difficult time understanding scientific advances, because of conflicting
information.

Back in 1983 – a very long time ago, if we refer to the progress
of molecular biology as a standard system for measuring time –
Al, an investment banker by training and the president of a newly
founded biotechnology company, was delivering a speech to potential
investors. If these speculators could be convinced of the validity of the
overall research and the benefits these business strategies presented to
them, they would contribute additional funds in the form of a private
partnership. Al was nervous, because the company's future depended
in part on the outcome of this fund-raising campaign. The investors
present at the meeting understandably wanted as much information
as possible about the company. Some comments were directly relevant
to the matter at hand, others were not.

'Why do you people want to create bigger rats?' a woman from
the audience asked. 'You see, my husband is an exterminator and
has enough problems already doing his job!'

In scientific research as in any other field, progress invariably
brings new trends. In 1983 speculation about increasing the size
of laboratory animals by genetic manipulation was a fashionable
subject. And the woman who had asked the question was certainly
puzzled by the accounts she had read in newspapers and magazines
about the so-called super-mice and super-rats.

Al was embarrassed, because he was unable to outline a proper
answer. He was the businessman of the company and at the time had
but little knowledge of the underlying scientific concepts necessary to
quickly elaborate a satisfactory explanation. So he had no alternative
but to come up with an off-hand remark – a social skill he had
developed to its maximum.

'Madam, bigger rats will be easier to shoot!' he replied.

His comment drew many laughs and helped to relax the atmosphere. Al eventually managed to convince everyone of the certain
success of the company, obtained the necessary investment and this
venture-capital company later flourished to the point of becoming
one of the world leaders.

I have heard several versions of this story, and although I do not
know which is true, it illustrates the problem of explaining to the

public at large ideas pertaining to molecular biology. The reason is quite simple. Molecular biology is a new discipline which is advancing at a very fast pace. Its sophisticated concepts are sometimes difficult to understand even for scientists in other disciplines. However, this should not be used as an excuse. Nothing is too complicated in molecular biology to be explained in simple terms, provided we fully understand what we want to explain. As the eighteenth-century philosopher Boileau said, '*Ce qui se conçoit bien s'énonce clairement.*'

Not surprisingly, many new terms and ideas of molecular biology have entered our vocabulary and way of thinking during the past decade. From DNA splicing to gene cloning, from new-generation drugs to genetic testing, from predicting an individual's genetic susceptibility to hereditary diseases to ethical questions raised by new genetics, from gene therapy to the eradication of infectious diseases, from milk-producing super-cows to ice-resistant plants, questions abound. These ideas no longer belong to the world of science fiction; they are a reality.

However, while the meanings of terms such as 'gene' and 'clone' are taken for granted by the media, several of my family members, friends and acquaintances keep on asking me the same inevitable questions: 'What is DNA? Is it where you find these "genes"? How can these transmit heredity and disease, and even character traits?' When I heard the same sorts of question put to me in a roundabout way by a famous West Coast psychiatrist, known for his research in the field of neuropharmacology, I realized just how fragmented our information in this area has become. We are torn between the desire to be informed and the time that we can devote towards understanding molecular biology.

I recognize that scientific discoveries, however important they may be, are always difficult to explain in simple terms. It is not easy to make them sound lively. To sell science to the public, the media often present the essence of research results in a form better suited to Hollywood movie scripts. Yet it is unnecessary to speculate or bend the truth to arouse public interest. All the classic ingredients are there: good and bad, conflicts and battles, epic saga of laboratories, laboratory teams and generations of scientists, victory and defeat, as well as the main driving force of human actions – greed (greed for money and fame on the part of universities and companies, greed for ephemeral fame and glory on the part of scientists, and greed for personal kudos on the part of pharmaceutical and biotechnology company managers). What a story!

In providing information to a public which legitimately wants answers to its questions, we should remain within the frame of what we know and present only reasonable hopes and expectations, not promise fantastic future applications simply to attract attention.

Are Diseases Unavoidable?

Since the most ancient times, devastating infectious diseases have always been the major cause of early death. Until this century, they were the main reason for short life expectancy, but now infectious diseases have been conquered. As a consequence, humans are living longer. Does this mean that illnesses have been brought under control? Not at all. New times bring new diseases – the 'modern' diseases that are also called, for lack of a better term and to hide our ignorance, 'multifactorial' diseases. That means that the progression of the disease results from the interplay between two different types of factor – environmental and genetic. Heart disease, cancer, asthma, osteoporosis and senile dementia are examples. People were always predisposed to today's most common diseases. In the past they did not live long enough to be affected by them, and they had not yet created environments and life styles which had adverse effects on their health. Compared to today's situation, the prevalence of these diseases remained low.

Molecular biology is the best new tool with which we can hope to decipher the extraordinary complexity of modern diseases. Although traditional medicine, principally interested in cure and treatment, has made spectacular progress over the last few decades, we are now entering an era of prevention, where the development of diagnostic and prognostic tests becomes a crucial step in the fight to improve the human condition. Molecular biology has introduced a new dimension to the medical revolution and is leading the race for preventive medicine.

Moreover, we now feel capable of deciphering the fundamental complexity of behaviour and evolution of living organisms, subjects which have puzzled human beings for as long as we know. It is encouraging to realize how new research methods, which are nothing but the logical continuation of the work carried out by countless generations of scientists and thinkers, give us hope for a better future by fighting devastating illnesses and thereby retarding the occurrence of what we fear the most because we understand it the least – death.

A major accomplishment of molecular biology is that disease appears less and less of a mystery. Not only do we now understand the molecular basis of many illnesses but we are also beginning to elaborate efficient forms of new treatment, such as new-generation drugs – molecules manufactured by genetic engineering. We are also slowly moving to a stage when we will be able to prevent serious disorders such as heart disease, cancer, AIDS and mental illnesses. We all want to know what we can reasonably expect and within what time frame.

By participating in the battle against disease, genetic manipulation contributes to an extension of life span, provided we also adopt a healthier mode of living. How should society react to a healthier existence, and indeed do governments have the right or the moral obligation to impose healthier life styles on their citizens? All aspects of day-to-day life will be affected by such decisions. A more pragmatic question is how insurance companies will react to the news that an individual applying for a life insurance policy presents a drastically increased risk of suffering a heart attack.

Nature *vs* Nurture

The influence of hereditary factors on our current approach to the phenomena implicated in life's processes is so well accepted that the term 'genetic' is used everywhere, from textbooks to media and daily conversations. I have often heard even experts say, 'Everything is genetic, except for being run over by a car.' This statement is not entirely correct – even being run over by a car includes a genetic component! Although the condition of the car, of the road and of the weather may be the most important factors, behavioural traits of the driver and of the victim, such as temper, ability to concentrate, eyesight and the effects of alcohol, are determined by genetic factors. Alcoholism has a well demonstrated major hereditary component and lack of attention can be the manifestation of several hereditary diseases. Compared to a genetic illness such as sickle cell anaemia, which is exclusively the result of a genetic abnormality, a road accident is due for a very small part only to the effect of hereditary factors which still cannot be entirely ignored.

The underlying principles of genetics have deeply affected our perception of life, so that over the past centuries there has been much debate about what rules human existence: is it heredity or environment? Here is the old debate, Nature *vs* Nurture.

We stand at the threshold of a new era of conceptualization which finally accepts a balanced view of the roles played by heredity and environment in defining the course of a human life in health and disease. What we are striving for at present is to understand the respective roles played by each of the two components, and how they interact with each other.

The Pace of Scientific Discoveries

The pace of advances in molecular biology is so fast that no one in this field can pretend to be able to keep track of what exactly is going on. So many discoveries are reported every week in the research literature that trying to follow even the landmarks has become too time-consuming for scientists already devoting all their energy to their own projects.

Of course, molecular biologists have had to narrow down the scope of their interests, just like scientists in other disciplines. Despite the ever-increasing specialization that has taken place, they can barely manage to keep abreast of the progress made in their own fields of investigation.

Since it first came out in 1965, James Watson's *Molecular Biology of the Gene* has been the bedside reading of molecular biologists. In 1965 one person could cope with the task of compiling a complete book on everything that was known about the DNA molecule. Not any more. It took four authors and no less than eighty-three main reviewers to compile the 1,163 pages of carefully selected breakthroughs for the two volumes of the fourth edition, published in 1987.

'Today no molecular biologist knows all the important facts about the gene' is the first sentence of the preface. This statement in itself sums up today's situation. In the same preface, the authors also add: 'Because of the immense breadth of today's research on the gene, none of us can speak with real authority except in those areas where our own research efforts are concentrated.'

We have come a long way from the image of the nineteenth-century biologists as we like to portray them in our minds. In those days they seemed to have all the time in the world to wander in the countryside, recording their observations and ideas in their diaries. They would gather research material and carry out their experiments in the peaceful surroundings of their laboratories. They would then write up results and draw conclusions – an undertaking that would sometimes take years. They could be expert in several distinct scientific disciplines at the same time, while being active in the fields of philosophy, literature and music too. In short, the nineteenth-century scientist is portrayed as the perfect Renaissance man.

Modern scientists have ample opportunity to reflect with nostalgia on such an enviable life style. In fact, it is this very image of the nineteenth-century savant that fascinated me when I was a child. It still does. However, reality today is very different. True, research is still as exhilarating as it has always been, but the rules of the game have changed. The frenzy to which it is sometimes difficult to adapt oneself has replaced yesterday's slower pace. The uneasy feeling of constantly running after time is but a side effect of the society we have modelled according to our needs, and is most certainly shared by all professionals in the Western world. We just have to learn how to live with it.

Society's Excesses

The contribution of molecular biology to fundamental research, to medicine and to society's way of life is intricately interwoven with the changes in the code of ethics that have occurred over the past two decades. The post-Second World War era was marked by a booming economy; its ethics were based on the cult of the family and of the community, on reaching individual achievement through hard work.

In contrast to this post-war boom, we have been experiencing for some time now slower economic growth, which has been accompanied by changes in cultural values and in individual life styles. Today the foundation of society lies in the cult of the self. The emphasis is on looks, appearance and staying fit. We are constantly searching for a proper balance between work and leisure. It may seem a paradox that although society has reached a stage of appreciable technological sophistication, the individual is looking to return to more natural ways of living. We admit the importance of respecting the environment, but realize the conflict generated between the ecological view and the effects of technological progress. With the questions it raises, biotechnology lies at the heart of the conflict.

These very principles of the post-war era, centred around the family nucleus and success through hard work, have led to the consumer society we live in, with goods in excess and material values as the driving force. In the Western world, profusion is found in all aspects of everyday life. For example, we have access to enormous amounts of information to the point where it is sometimes difficult to make sound business and personal decisions, or to understand what is happening in the rest of the world. In this respect, excessive information becomes confusing because it overloads our brain capacity. Confronted with too many choices, we tend to fall back on primitive brain structures and shut off from reality. Hence the popularity of television. Through a similar mechanism, people tend to seek refuge in irrational shelters. But what may originally be a need to believe in something that cannot be rationally explained, an urge to feel overwhelmed by mysticism, has led to a paradox.

Scientific advances provide the individual with an increasing number of means to detect, treat and cure illnesses, but they also generate a complexity that makes disease mechanisms – and associated forms of treatment – more difficult to understand. In part because of the growing difficulty of understanding these concepts, an increasing number of individuals put more faith in alternative medicines, ranging from pseudo-scientific disciplines whose healers reject the very principles of medicine but insist on being called 'doctors' to associations formed by entrepreneurs with dubious credentials who take full advantage of people's gullibility and feelings of hopelessness. This is not to dismiss the often valuable work done by practitioners of alternative therapies. Today is no different from any other time. Science keeps on fighting its battle against the doubts raised by society's irrational fears.

The Human Power

Scientists have discovered new avenues leading to an ocean of possibilities awaiting exploration. They also possess the materials to embark on such expeditions. Whether from mere curiosity or an eagerness to learn, we all want to know what we can reasonably expect. We want to have some idea about the time scale involved, because the developments that lie ahead will inevitably change society's attitude towards human disease and human behaviour. We all feel concerned about the implications of these fantastic realities and about the impact of these methods on our daily lives.

We can modify our environment. We have in fact done it extensively and continue to do so every day. We can create our own environment in choosing to adopt our own life style. We are free to decide what direction we want to take. Our genetic blueprint, however, is the product of a combination, a mosaic of genes inherited from our parents. Until now, we had no control over this random distribution. The genetic material we have been awarded is the result of a lottery, the lottery of life.

Today we have the power to manipulate the genetic material at will, to modify what it took Nature 4.5 billion years to create. These are exciting but scary times. Opponents of recombinant DNA technology do not hesitate to accuse scientists of treating life like a game. However, as exciting as it might be, new genetics is not a game. We have the capacity to cure, to prevent and to eliminate devastating diseases. We have the possibility of alleviating suffering. Will we manage to use the extraordinary tools we have forged for a good cause – a better future?

PART ONE

Genetic Blueprint and Genetic Markers – a Matter of Evolution

1

Where Does Life Begin?

IN 1953 FRANCIS CRICK AND JAMES WATSON (WHO WERE AWARDED the Nobel Prize for Medicine and Physiology in 1962) published a short article in the prestigious British journal *Nature*. In it they described the results of their research (and also their frantic race against both time and other research teams) into the structure of the deoxyribonucleic acid (DNA) molecule. The work, which was conducted between 1950 and 1953, did not go smoothly – research never does – and was marred by conflicts with both colleagues and administrators. Accounts of this exciting period in the history of science are related in several books, including James Watson's *Double Helix* and, more recently, John Gribbin's *In Search of the Double Helix*.

The DNA molecule fascinates scientists and non-scientists alike, because it is the molecule of life. It directs the production of every protein, thus orchestrating all the biochemical reactions characteristic of living organisms. Its real beauty, however, lies in its symmetrical structure: two complementary strands are intertwined into the shape of a left-handed double helix.

In many cultures symmetry is considered to be the closest representation of perfection. In the Japanese city of Kyoto there is a temple whose entrance comprises two perfectly symmetrical wooden doors with breathtakingly elaborate carvings. However, they are only almost perfectly symmetrical, for the sculptors voluntarily introduced a humble flaw – so tiny that it is barely visible – so that the masterpiece would 'not upset the Gods'. 'Perfectly symmetrical arrangement' is a phrase frequently used to characterize the DNA molecule. As for the Japanese temple's doors, there are a few tiny flaws, but these have been introduced by Nature.

Where Is DNA in our Body?

At first it is difficult to put things into perspective and understand where the DNA molecules are within an organism. They belong to the microscopic world, which means that they are invisible to the naked eye. So where *are* they?

Our body is made up of different organs and tissues, such as skin, brain, liver, muscles and bones. Each of these in turn is an assemblage of millions and millions of fundamental, microscopic, specialized and differentiated components: the cells. Thus the brain is a package of brain cells, the liver of liver cells, and so on. Fundamentally cells are factories where all biochemical reactions take place. They are said to be differentiated; indeed, liver cells, for example, direct all their energy to producing liver enzymes, implicated in food digestion, while brain cells synthesize neurotransmitters (molecules permitting the conduction and transmission of nerve messages).

If their function depends on the organ they are a part of, the overall structure of a cell is constant: a cellular membrane isolates cellular constituents, whose function is to manufacture specific cellular products such as neurotransmitters, enzymes involved in digestion and in energy storage, and hormones. A cell also contains a nucleus, isolated from the cellular machinery by a nuclear membrane, in which we find a DNA molecule orchestrating the day-to-day life of the cell, telling it what to produce and directing the successive cell-division processes.

Although it might be conceptually easier to examine what is readily visible first – that is, the whole body – and then gradually switch to the organ, the cell and the DNA molecule, it makes more sense scientifically to start with the DNA molecule itself, because that is what directs all the phenomena observed in the body.

The Structure of Genetic Material

Each of the two strands of the human DNA molecule is itself made up of a continuous, linear sequence of 3 billion fundamental building-blocks, the nucleotides. Each nucleotide is in turn composed of three constituents: a sugar molecule (called deoxyribose), a phosphate molecule and a base. Both the deoxyribose and the phosphate molecules are invariant; what differentiate the nucleotides from one another are the bases.

Surely, then, there must be a very large number of bases? Not at all. There are only four types, called adenine, cytosine, guanine and thymine, generally represented by their first letters: A, C, G and T.

It is a remarkable fact that all living organisms exist because of DNA molecules constituted by linear arrangements of only four types of nucleotide. To create humans nature has constructed a chain of 3 billion links, starting with just four different kinds of link!

The principle seems so elegant and yet is so extraordinary that it is worth using an analogy to make sure we really understand. The human DNA molecule can be compared to a book containing 3 billion characters but written with only four different characters. One of the main goals of molecular biologists is to be able to read this Book of Life.

As the DNA molecule is invisible to the naked eye, scientists need a powerful electron microscope to observe its overall structure. It is packed, coiled and folded in on itself within the cell nucleus, visible only with the magnification achieved by a regular microscope, yet when the DNA chain contained in each of our cells is stretched into linear form, its length is about 2 metres.

The complementarity of the two strands of DNA molecules results from specific pairing of the bases: thus the A in one chain always pairs with a T in the opposite strand, and the C always pairs with a G. The length of the DNA molecule is therefore expressed in terms of numbers of base pairs rather than of nucleotides. We say that a given DNA region is ten base pairs, or 12,000 base pairs long.

It is DNA that is passed on from one generation to the next. This is why the DNA molecule is also referred to as genetic, or hereditary, material. The complementarity of the two strands forms the basis for the transmission of genetic information. To comprehend how this works, it is necessary to talk first about cells.

Cells Divide into Their Clones

A living organism such as the human body is made up of billions and billions of fundamental constituents: the cells. The total number of cells (rough estimates suggest 60 trillion, which is 60,000 billion, or 60 million million) is so enormous that it is difficult to comprehend the sort of scale involved. This might help you. Thirty years ago I was told that if each cell of our body was a brick, we would be able to build the equivalent of the Great Wall of China round the world seventeen times!

Each living organism is composed of a predetermined number of cells whose size is independent of the size of the animal or plant. Some mouse cells are larger than others from an elephant. Different organs of the same organism have cells of different sizes. Their diameter generally varies between one-tenth and one-hundredth of a millimetre. The cellular membrane is permeable and permits the exchange of smaller chemical compounds with the rest of the organism.

Cells are living structures. Not only do they grow but they also constitute factories where a large number of biochemical reactions take place and signals are exchanged with other cells. Their distinct property is the ability to divide. Indeed, all the cells of the organism originate from one single cell – the egg – by a series of successive divisions. Except for highly differentiated cells, such as nerve cells, they all continue to grow and divide throughout the life of the individual. The process of cell division is particularly obvious when we think of phenomena as diverse as skin regeneration, wound healing and hair or nail growth.

All cells of the human body (with the exception of red blood cells) have a nucleus containing a DNA molecule (the rest of the cell is called the cytoplasm). When a cell divides its DNA is duplicated so that each of the two daughter cells contains exactly the same genetic information. This is possible because of the complementarity of the two strands of the DNA molecule. During nuclear division the two DNA strands separate, and each of them serves as a template for the making of its complementary chain. Indeed, as a result of specific base pairing, each chain dictates the synthesis of its complement. The nuclear division thus generates two DNA molecules that are identical to each other and to the DNA that was present in the original cell. The extent of DNA synthesis in our body is simply phenomenal: 300 million miles of DNA are produced every day – the distance between the earth and the sun!

Science-fiction fans have based many stories on the fact that all cells of an organism contain identical genetic material. For example, it could thus be possible to make clones (twin copies) of a person from any cell of his or her body. Researchers from a private Canadian company have already conducted such an experiment on animals; they have made a small herd of cows by manufacturing clones from the cells of an early embryo. When asked by the press if this could be possible in humans, they answered: 'Yes, but there is no market for it!' Since then, by using the same technique called multiplication of embryos by transfer of nuclei for engineering clones, researchers have obtained sets of 9 and 12 cows, 4 sheep and 6 rabbits. In the near future, we expect that scientists will apply this method to the selection of specific traits of particular economical interest – animals with 'more beef', higher quality meat, increased milk production, eggs with tougher shells, genetic resistance to disease.

While some argue that such a selection tends towards uniformity, i.e. that we will reduce natural genetic diversity, others advance that this same technique will allow us to preserve frozen embryos bearing traits that have become extremely rare and would otherwise tend to disappear.

The Chromosomes

DNA molecules can be observed during specific times within the periods of cell division. They contract, becoming much thicker, and are easily stained with chemical dyes. They form structures which are identifiable through high-powered microscopes and are called the chromosomes.

Each individual chromosome is formed by two arms of unequal length (a short arm, referred to as 'p' by geneticists, and a long arm, called 'q'), attached together by a structure called the centromere. Chromosomes exist in pairs, so the genetic material is made up of two identical sets of chromosomes. The 3 billion base pairs comprising human genetic material, for example, are visible as a total of forty-six chromosomes: twenty-two pairs of autosomes (non-sexual chromosomes) and a pair of sex chromosomes. The female genetic material bears a pair of X chromosomes; her chromosome composition is labelled 46,XX. In males the pair of sex chromosomes is composed of one X and one Y chromosome; male chromosome typing is 46,XY. Therefore, at the genetic level the only difference between a woman and a man lies in the replacement of one X by one Y chromosome!

Proteins Are Good for You

The genetic material is the organizer of the reactions making life possible. To that end it directs the production of proteins. Proteins are very large molecules, called 'macromolecules'. As with DNA, they are constituted by specific, continuous sequences of basic building-blocks. In this case, however, the basic links of the protein chain are molecules called 'amino acids', of which there are twenty different types (as opposed to only four different types of nucleotide in nucleic acids).

There are probably about 100,000 different proteins in our body, (the most recent estimates range from 50,000 to 100,000) although we have discovered only a fraction of these. Some examples are insulin (a hormone), the keratin of the skin, the collagen of the tendons, haemoglobin found inside red blood cells and apolipoproteins, proteins that are part of the lipoprotein particles, which are involved in lipid transport and metabolism.

Proteins participate actively in all the biochemical reactions (metabolism) characteristic of living organisms. Once synthesized, they either remain within the cell or are secreted outside the cell and can go anywhere in the body to carry out their functions. Some of them have a structural role; others are enzymes, molecules making possible many diverse types of biochemical reactions (energy constraints would prevent these reactions occurring otherwise). Many hormones are protein molecules. Proteins can also act as receptors or transporters for other molecules. Binding between a receptor protein and its ligand constitutes a powerful signal, triggering a whole series of other reactions in the body. Last but not least, human DNA in the cell is itself coated with many different types of protein, and the chromosomes that we observe are constituted of a mixture of DNA and proteins (this is why they are also called deoxyribonucleoprotein fibres).

What Are Genes?

The production of proteins is under the control of DNA. The DNA molecule is organized into regions coding for the making of proteins. These specific sequences constitute the genes. One gene codes for one particular protein. Since there may be as many as 100,000 proteins, there are also about 100,000 genes scattered all along the human genome (the total DNA).

It was initially thought that the human genome was constituted by a complete set of consecutive genes in a head-to-tail arrangement. Molecular biologists, however, soon realized that this simple – though plausible – model was wrong. The total number of suspected genes does not account for the total number of nucleotides constituting the human genome. The genome contains long stretches of DNA in between the genes. (Some of these apparently functionless sequences have at times been called 'junk DNA'.) Genes are thus interspersed throughout the DNA molecule, and we still do not know the reason for the presence of intergenic regions. There are indications that the existence of sequences found a short way ahead of all genes is necessary for a sufficient and sustained expression of the genes located a few tens of nucleotides further on. Scientists have also assumed for a long time the presence of 'enhancers' – DNA sequences which help to increase the expression of downstream genes – ahead of the gene. The existence of most of the intergenic sequences, however, remains a mystery that scientists are actively trying to solve.

Genes are made up of variable numbers of base pairs. The length of the genes which have already been characterized varies between a few hundred base pairs and, for the largest one, 2 million base pairs (this gene codes for a protein called 'dynorphin', and we know that abnormalities of this protein are responsible for a devastating disease, Duchenne's myopathy). On average, genes are a few thousand nucleotides long.

Not only the lengths but also the sequences of the genes vary. How do we identify a gene from its surrounding DNA? When we read the sequence of a DNA stretch known to encompass a gene, it is just a succession of nucleotides; nowhere does the word 'gene' seem to be mentioned at its exact location. In fact, it is, and we just need to be taught how to read DNA language. Molecular biologists have learned to recognize key sequences which define the boundaries as well as several internal portions of a gene. These are almost invariant among all the genes that have been isolated. It is thus relatively easy to detect and localize a gene when reading a DNA sequence.

From Genes to Proteins: A Tortuous Path?

Genes do not conduct the synthesis of proteins directly. They do so through the intermediary of messengers, called messenger ribonucleic acids, or mRNAs. These are almost identical copies of isolated genes, except that the sugar molecule is a ribose instead of a deoxyribose (the difference between the two is very small, involving the addition of one atom of oxygen on the molecule of deoxyribose) and thymine is replaced by another base, uracyl. During what is called the transcription phase the gene is copied into its single-stranded counterpart, the mRNA. The mRNA molecule undergoes some modifications (we say that it is processed), but its sequence remains the exact replica of the corresponding coding sequence of the gene. The mRNA is transported from the nucleus to the cytoplasm of the cell, where it is read by sophisticated machinery responsible for the making of proteins.

The protein sequence is dictated by the sequence of the mRNA in a process called 'translation'. The key to the reading is contained in what is called the 'genetic code'. As far as codes go, the genetic code is straightforward: the mRNA is read in a continuous fashion by blocks of three consecutive nucleotides called 'triplets' or 'codons'. Each codon corresponds to one particular amino acid. For example, a succession of three adenines (AAA) on the mRNA corresponds to a phenylalanine; GAG codes for glutamic acid; and AAG for lysine.

Amino acids do not recognize the codons directly. These are read by another type of RNA called transfer RNA (tRNA). One end of a tRNA carries a particular amino acid while another part is constituted by a well-exposed triplet of bases that matches complementary codons on mRNAs. The mRNA is read in a zipper-like fashion: a first tRNA binds to its complementary codon, then a second, then a third, until the end of the sequence. The amino acids at the other end of the tRNAs, put in contact with each other, react to make up the protein chain.

We Are Not Immortal

All cells are constantly working at the numerous and uninterrupted biochemical reactions that represent life's processes. The same types of reaction take place in all living organisms, whatever their degree of evolution. The simplest life forms are actually unicellular (single cell) organisms, such as bacteria and protozoa, and the existence of over 20,000 of them (their observation requires a microscope) has been reported. The fantastic advantage they have over multicellular organisms like us is the possibility of unlimited life: if environmental conditions are favourable, they can divide endlessly, each cell always producing two daughter cells (the term 'daughter cell' is merely a trick of language, since these cells are neither male nor female; it designates cells resulting from the division of a 'parent cell'). Muticellular organisms (composed of many cells) such as human beings have a limited lifespan. Only germ cells, which are somehow transmitted to the offspring, possess the potential immortality of unicellular bodies. All other cells of the body (somatic cells) are destined to disappear without trace.

The Two Types of Cell Division

Germ cells and somatic cells undergo different sorts of division. Somatic cells divide by the process previously outlined, called mitosis (from the Greek *mitos*, meaning thread), whereby one parent cell divides into two daughter cells. The whole process takes anywhere between a few minutes and a few hours, depending on the cell type and the temperature at which division occurs. Each chromosome divides into two identical copies so that the number and structure of chromosomes in each of the two daughter cells are the same as in the parent nucleus. Germ cells (or gametes, or sex cells) divide by meiosis (from the Greek *meion*, meaning less). Through this process, the original two million immature eggs contained in a woman's ovaries at birth transform at puberty into mature eggs (ova) that are ready for fecundation, and sperms (or spermatozoa) are produced in the tubules of a man's testicles at the rate of one thousand per second.

Meiosis involves two successive cell divisions while the chromosomes divide only once. The final result is the making, from one parent cell, of four cells instead of two; each of them, however, receives either one of the sets of homologous chromosomes. Ova and sperms thus contain what is referred to as a haploid number of chromosomes (instead of twenty-five pairs in somatic cells). Meiosis constitutes a crucial stage in evolution, because it is when meiotic recombination occurs.

What is genetic recombination? During the earliest phases of meiosis, the pairs of chromosomes inherited from an individual's father and mother first divide by mitosis to produce two identical cells, which then divide twice more by meiosis. At that time, the pairs of dividing homologous chromosomes (those from the father and those from the mother) remain in close contact and lie alongside. They interlace, cross over, break and reconnect, at which time they will have swopped chromosomal segments with their counterparts. Through this process of genetic recombination (or crossing over), portions of genetic materials are thus exchanged between paternal and maternal DNAs. The end result is that, in germ cells, crossing over creates new chromosomes constituted by a mosaic of the parent chromosomes. Given the length of the DNA molecule, the number of genetic combinations is extraordinarily large, and the reshuffled genetic material, which is transmitted to the offspring, is different in all germ cells. Naturally, genes that are far apart on a given chromosome are more likely to become separated by recombination than genes that are close by; the greater the physical distance between two loci, the more room for DNA segments to cross over.

The Molecular Clock of the Cells

All cells, whether somatic or germ, constantly oscillate between two states: growth and division. After division a cell grows until some signal tells it to divide again. This process is so precise and well controlled that scientists have long speculated concerning the existence of an internal oscillator, some kind of sophisticated molecular clock that times and orchestrates the successive periods of growth and division.

Apart from suspecting its existence, we knew nothing about this molecular clock for a long time. Several research projects, however, have started to unveil some of these mysterious mechanisms, and we know now that this oscillator is composed of several molecules, some of which have been isolated and characterized. Among them scientists have identified several proteins, including one called p34cdc2 (not a very manageable name!) and cyclins.

The molecular clock represents such a fundamental mechanism that it has been preserved unchanged through millions of years of evolution. Indeed, the study of these proteins in different animal species has led to a remarkable conclusion: they are almost identical in organisms ranging from yeast to humans. Of course, we still have a lot to learn, and the discovery of the oscillator's other constituents will permit us to understand more of how this complex system works.

Differentiation: A Form of Specialization

All the cells of the human body originate from a unique cell and contain exactly the same genetic material. Yet they go their different ways to live their different lives, forming different organs: some make up the skin; others the bones, or the brain, or the liver, or any part of the body. Through a process of differentiation, different genes are expressed in different cell lines.

Red cells of the blood are mainly haemoglobin factories. They do synthesize many other proteins, but mostly they become like little bags filled with haemoglobin, the protein responsible for transporting oxygen to and removing carbon dioxide from the various tissues of the body. Neurons (brain and nerve cells) produce neurotransmitters, whose function is to convey signals between nerve cells. Pancreatic cells manufacture enzymes whose main role is to participate in digestion processes; those making up a readily identifiable part of the pancreas called Langerhans Islet synthesize insulin, a hormone regulating blood sugar levels in the organism as well as influencing cellular mobilization of triglycerides. And so on with all the organs.

A living organism is an admirable machine with precise functions regulated by specific and finely tuned control mechanisms. Molecular biology makes it possible to study directly the genes responsible for the existence and the smooth-running of this machine. It has given an additional boost to classical biology, which aims to understand how each cell and each organ operate. When looking at the complexity of all the reactions taking place in a human body, I often wonder how it is that so few errors are made. Coming back to cell division, for example, how do we always end up with the right number of cells and very seldom with a random proliferation (a cancer)? There lies the real beauty of a living organism. We are beginning to understand better how it all works – and why it sometimes does not. The fine line between the two is one of my recurring themes here.

2

The World of Gene Splicers

IT IS NOW TIME TO SPEAK OF GENETIC ENGINEERING, A FIELD WHICH deals specifically with the techniques of molecular biology that permit DNA manipulation. We are basically talking about the ability to cut DNA at specific locations, to piece DNA fragments together and to replicate and express them in different organisms.

Nothing looks more like one DNA molecule than another DNA molecule. DNA from all species of organism is constituted by linear arrangements of nucleotides. Recombinant DNA techniques thus operate across species. It is as easy to cut and piece together human DNA fragments as it is to cut and piece together human and bacteria, horse and monkey or human and fly DNA fragments. It is this ability to engineer hybrid DNAs which do not occur naturally that has led to so much controversy between molecular biologists and their opponents.

Restriction Endonucleases:
A Barbarian Name to Splice DNA

The most basic and most useful tools of genetic engineering are restriction endonucleases. These enzymes cut double-stranded DNA at specific permutations of nucleotides – the restriction sites. Restriction endonucleases are found in bacteria, where they probably participate in defence against the invasion of viruses; in fact, they chop offencing viral DNAs that would otherwise kill the bacterial cells.

Since the early 1970s, when they were first used following the work of the Americans Stanley Cohen and Herb Boyer, about 300 different restriction endonucleases have been reported, and they all recognize their own signature sequence. They are named by the first letters of the micro-organisms in which they are found. The restriction endonuclease EcoRI, for example, is isolated from bacteria coating human intestines called *Escherichia coli*. EcoRI cuts DNA molecules at all locations where the signature sequence GAATTC occurs. The restriction site of PstI (from *Pseudomonas stuartii*) is CTGCAG, and that of MspI (*Moraxella* sp.), CCGG. Restriction sites are generally composed of four to six base pairs. Statistically, a combination of four nucleotides occurs more frequently than a combination of six nucleotides. This is why a six-base cutter (a term used in the jargon of molecular biologists to designate a restriction enzyme whose recognition site is composed of six base pairs) generates about 1 million fragments and a four-base cutter, about 10 million fragments upon 'digesting' a human DNA molecule.

Their ability to cut DNA at specific locations has led to restriction endonucleases being called molecular scissors. Many artistic representations show DNA as a ribbon being cut with little scissors and this image is quite faithful to what goes on at the molecular level.

Gene Cloning: Piecing Together DNA Fragments and Mass Production of These Fragments

Individual DNA fragments can be pieced together with the help of another fundamental enzyme for molecular biologists, DNA ligase. With ligase any DNA fragment of any given length and sequence can be added to another. Since DNA molecules from all living organisms always have the same basic chemical structure, DNA segments isolated from different animal species can be attached to each other as easily as segments from the same species. This fundamental property forms the basis of what is referred to as 'gene cloning'.

Gene cloning comprises isolating a fragment of the DNA molecule of a given species and introducing this fragment into DNA of another species in order to generate *in vitro* a very large number of copies of the original fragment. This fragment may be any part of the genome, including a gene, but it does not necessarily have to be a gene; it can be a DNA sequence of no known function.

To make unlimited numbers of copies of a fragment of interest, molecular biologists can choose between several replication systems. It all depends on the size of the fragment. The most widely used of replication systems are plasmids, which are short, self-replicating DNA units contained within bacteria. In a single bacterial cell one plasmid can replicate into thousands of copies. Bacteria themselves can be made to divide indefinitely. The general cloning strategy can thus be summed up in a few sentences. With the help of restriction endonucleases and ligase, a human DNA fragment is cloned into a bacterial plasmid. This 'hybrid' DNA molecule is then reintroduced into bacteria that grow and divide on nutritive media in the laboratory. Billions of copies of the hybrid plasmid are thus generated. Several techniques developed by molecular biologists allow the isolation in a pure form of large amounts of the original fragment.

Plasmids are best used with DNA sequences up to 15,000 base pairs long. Longer fragments require other systems, but the basic principle remains the same: introduction of a piece of DNA in a replicating unit generating billions of copies of the original piece. Other systems include bacteriophages, or viruses which replicate in bacteria; synthetic hybrids of plasmid and phage DNAs, known as cosmids; and yeast artificial chromosomes.

DNA Libraries

Cloning techniques allow molecular biologists to make two types of DNA libraries – genomic libraries and cDNA libraries. To obtain a genomic library, an entire genome (human or otherwise) is cut with restriction endonucleases into about 1 million fragments. Each of these fragments is individually cloned into plasmid DNAs, phage DNAs or as artificial chromosomes in yeast cells, so that the complete DNA molecule is available as a set of smaller pieces which are easier to handle experimentally. They represent all the books of a complete library. Every piece can be indefinitely replicated in the laboratory. Any particular fragment of interest can be isolated for individual study. To pull it out, scientists use radioactively labelled DNA probes whose sequences are complementary to that of the targeted fragment. The radioactive tag allows the detection of fragments hybridized to the DNA probe, which can then be selectively pulled out of the genomic library.

In the case of the cDNA (complementary DNA) library, different genes (from a few to a few hundred) are expressed in different cells. In liver cells, only genes coding for liver enzymes are active. Red blood cells produce mostly haemoglobin but also several other enzymes necessary to red blood cell metabolism and function. Unfortunately, it is likely that particular genes of interest for study may not have been identified. To circumvent this problem, scientists can readily isolate the mRNAs from any specific tissue and construct their complementary DNAs – the original genes from which these mRNAs were transcribed. To achieve this, they use the enzyme reverse transcriptase, which copies mRNAs into their double-stranded DNA counterparts. These biochemically synthesized DNA fragments are called cDNAs. All cDNAs from any given tissue can be cloned into plasmid or phage vectors. Tissue-specific libraries are especially useful tools for the study and isolation of particular genes expressed in the corresponding tissues.

Polymerase Chain Reaction

The technique of polymerase chain reaction (PCR) is the major innovation of the past few years. PCR allows the amplification (the making of thousands of copies) of any given sequence of interest in the genome.

If we know what sequence to look for, we can use a DNA fragment as a probe at or near the site of this genomic region and generate, with the enzyme DNA polymerase (which replicates DNA into DNA), successions of copies of the sequence. The advantage is two-fold: first, scientists can obtain large DNA amounts of a specific sequence and thus greatly simplify the subsequent experimental steps; and second, minute amounts of DNA that would otherwise be too small for experiments can be amplified according to need.

A practical application of PCR concerns the field of genetic testing. It is possible to determine the sex of an embryo only three days after fecundation, as reported in a 1989 issue of the British medical weekly the *Lancet*. Scientists isolated one cell of a three-day-old embryo (then made up of six to ten cells) which had been obtained after *in vitro* fertilization. They used a DNA probe for a region of the Y (male) chromosome. If a fragment is detected after amplification of the DNA, it means that the embryo is a male. If no fragment is present, it means that there is no Y chromosome and that the embryo is thus a female.

A direct application could conceivably be early diagnosis of sex-linked genetic abnormalities. However, the fear of abuse of this technology might inhibit its widespread application.

How About Genetic Diseases?

Genetic diseases are caused by abnormalities at the DNA level which result in abnormal or absent corresponding proteins. The structural and functional properties of an abnormal, or mutant, protein are modified. The deleterious (pathological) effects of a mutant protein can range from very little or no observable manifestations to lethal diseases. It all depends on what protein is affected and to what extent.

The total absence of a protein results in the missing of a major function and is generally a serious condition. Palliative treatments offered by traditional medicine treat the peripheral effects of the abnormality on the organism. In theory, however, there should be two ideal interventions: first, providing the natural protein to the organism; and second, replacing the defective gene with a normal, healthy one.

These two sorts of interventions – recombinant DNA drugs and gene therapy – are the fields of application of molecular biology that have generated the greatest hope but also the most intense ethical debates.

Recombinant DNA Drugs

It all started in the early 1970s when Stanley Cohen and Herb Boyer inserted frog genes into plasmids of the bacterial species *Escherichia coli*, wondering whether they would be expressed. The experiment was a success. The bacteria did produce mRNAs coding for proteins which until then had been produced only in frogs.

The genetic engineering revolution had started. Henceforward, humans could introduce any gene from any organism into cells grown in the laboratory and direct the production of the corresponding proteins. These cells act as factories that can be made to synthesize the protein coded by the cloned gene continuously.

The expression of human genes has permitted the isolation of pure human proteins, which are used in preference to synthetic drugs for patients who lack these proteins. In 1982 human insulin, used in the treatment of diabetes, was the first recombinant DNA drug approved by the US Food and Drug Administration (FDA), the organization that has the power to grant or block the introduction of a drug on to the market. Before 1982 the only insulin available was isolated from the pancreas of cattle or pigs; since then several other recombinbant DNA drugs have reached or are about to reach the market. Among them we can cite tissue-specific plasminogen activator (tPA), a blood-clot dissolving enzyme which reduces tissue damage after heart attacks and prevents subsequent heart attacks; growth hormone used in the treatment of some forms of dwarfism; alpha-interferon, which breaks down tumours among people affected with one form of cancer called hairy-cell leukaemia; a vaccine against B-hepatitis; and erythropoeitin, a hormone produced by the kidneys whose function is to stimulate the production of red blood cells, thereby making a preferred drug in the treatment of certain anaemias.

The major advantage in using human proteins produced by

recombinant DNA technology is that they are natural drugs in the sense that they constitute molecules normally produced by the human body itself; they are natural agents, recognized as such by the organism. In the future it will be possible to produce all natural human proteins by these techniques. At the moment the only limiting factor is the number of genes that have been isolated: at the most, only a few thousand of the 100,000 or so that are known to exist.

Although recombinant DNA drugs were originally seen by commercial companies as outstanding money-makers, profits have been lower than expected. These new types of drug are very expensive, so reducing the cost is one of the major goals of pharmaceutical companies. It takes on average about seven years to gain official approval for a new drug, and this has already been fatal to several organizations (Chapter 16 considers the commercial situation in its analysis of the future for biotechnology companies).

Gene Therapy

Among all the techniques developed by molecular biologists, the one that has started the biggest debates is gene therapy. The idea is to correct a genetic abnormality by replacing a disease gene with a normal gene. What is at first sight a fantastic way of curing illness has turned out to be a complex moral and ethical issue: to correct human genetic material is to correct what God – or Nature – has created.

There are two types of gene therapy. The first involves the manipulation of an egg or an early embryo, which means the correction of the genetic material will then occur in all the cells of the subsequent organism and also be transmitted to the offspring. The second consists of manipulating the genome of somatic (non-sexual) cells, the aim being to correct the genetic make-up of a given cell line of an individual; here the modification introduced is not transmitted to the next generations. At present genetic manipulations on human embryos are banned, while those on somatic cells are permitted only under stringent conditions.

Genetic therapy is a very promising tool of the future. Genetic counselling will undoubtedly contribute to decrease the number of births of individuals who are severely affected with genetic disorders – we have been witnessing such a regression in the case of hereditary forms of anaemia called beta-thalassemiae. We know, however, that we will not eradicate genetic disease with public education alone. Genetic therapy constitutes the ultimate weapon towards that end.

Several improvements, however, are necessary before this technology can be applied clinically on a routine basis. To insert gene-containing DNA sequences into a host cell's DNA, scientists use preferentially retroviruses (these particular viruses integrate their own genetic material into the genome of the cells that they infect). Engineering a retroviral vector involves replacing the portion of DNA coding for the viral proteins, which represents up to 80 per cent of the virus's genetic material, with the foreign DNA sequence to be inserted. With the help of retroviral vectors, researchers should be able to introduce any gene or DNA fragment into human cells.

Until now, researchers have mostly carried out their experiments on rapidly dividing cells such as bone marrow cells – cells of the haematopoietic (blood precursor) system – and fibroblasts (skin cells). They have succeeded in transfecting bone marrow cells from mice, primates and humans with retroviral vectors containing several different genes. They, however, are not yet technically able to replace precisely one gene with another one at a given genomic location. The success of integration of foreign genes in a cell's genome follows the laws of statistics; furthermore, these genes are, at best, randomly integrated. To make matters worse, the yield of integration is extremely low. Besides, some cells express foreign genes while others do not, and we still do not know the reason for that.

Genetic therapy is in fact part of what is called 'gene transfer'. After much debate, the first gene transfer experiment was approved in America by the National Institute of Health (NIH)'s Recombinant DNA Advisory Committee (or RAC), which grants scientists whose experiments involve DNA manipulation the authorization to start their research programmes, in early 1989. The experiment was proposed by W. French Anderson, R. Michael Blaese and Steven A. Rosenberg and sought to investigate the efficacy of gene transfer in the treatment of cancer tumours. The idea was to introduce a bacterial antibiotic-resistant gene into tumour-infiltrating lymphocytes (TIL), specific types of human lymphocytes implicated in the attack on cancer tumours.

TILs from cancer patients were isolated, grown in culture and activated with a specific cell activator called Interleukin-2, and antibiotic-resistant genes were integrated in TIL genomes. The TILs were then injected into the same patients. To determine how much they had infiltrated the tumours, bits of tumours were removed and checked for the presence of the antibiotic-resistant gene – a quick way to find the exact location of the TILs.

The first experiments on somatic cells to study the treatment of genetic diseases by genetic therapy was approved in America in July 1990. A special panel of experts called by members of the RAC gave the green light to a proposal by Steven A. Rosenberg and his team from the National Cancer Institute, in which they proposed a method based on gene therapy to treat children with a very rare inherited disease called adenosine deaminase deficiency, in which affected cells do not manufacture this enzyme, which is vital to the immune reactions of the organism. Today's treatment of the illness consists of regular injections of the missing enzyme, but it does not always work and the immune system can remain deficient. What Rosenberg intends to do is remove patients' white blood cells every month, insert the missing gene in these isolated cells and then reinject the transformed cells into the patients. This form of somatic-cell therapy is thus a new form of treatment, not a cure for the disease.

Both the constitution of NIH's Human Gene Therapy Subcommittee and the launch of a scientific journal called *Gene Therapy* testify to the growing importance of this field. Today, the first priority remains the correction of single, monogenic disorders by inserting the right gene at the right place, a task that is far from being achieved. Ultimately, however, gene transfer experiments offer a wider range of applications. They include the introduction of low-density lipoprotein receptor genes into liver cells to decrease cholesterol levels of individuals whose genetic susceptibility puts them at higher risk of developing atherosclerotic heart disease, the use of anti-clotting agents to facilitate tissue grafting, and the insertion of anti-cancer genes such as cytokines into the DNA of TILs of individuals who have higher cancer risks.

The most bothersome worry prevailing at this point in time stems from the danger that a foreign gene can combine with genomic regions containing oncogenes. Such a combination would, in some cases, be the trigger of initial reactions leading to cancer. This and other unpredicted complications impose strict restrictions to ensure the safety of research on gene transfer.

Gene Transfer and Animal Experimentation

Rather than experiment directly on humans, scientists have had no choice until now but to use animal models to study the development of human cancers and to test various drugs. The implication is that what happens in animals happens the same way in humans. These experiments can involve the making of 'transgenic' animals, such as the 'oncomice' marketed by Dupont de Nemours. To engineer an oncomice, a given human oncogen is inserted into a mouse egg's DNA. The transformed egg is then reintroduced in a mouse's uterus and the embryo develops normally except that it carries in its genome the human oncogen, whose effects can be studied under various sets of experimental conditions.

The methods developed by molecular biologists have been of tremendous value because they allow scientists to get away from animal experimentation. Indeed, scientists are gradually becoming able to test the effects of a drug or any other product directly on the concerned cells, grown in laboratory conditions. Refinements of these techniques should reach the point of making experiments on laboratory animals obsolete.

Molecular Biology: A Fashionable Undertaking

As early as the 1970s molecular biologists anticipated the repercussions their methods would have. The moral issues being raised led several experts to arrange a conference, and in 1975, at Asilomar on the California coast, about 100 miles south of San Francisco, molecular biologists reached a major decision: they agreed upon guidelines to govern recombinant DNA research.

Henceforward, all such experiments would be closely monitored by government organizations and take into account the concerns of the general public. Maybe for the first time in the history of biology, scientists themselves decided to slow down their research and pursue their work only after approval by independent committees. Since 1975 governments and political organizations from all countries undertaking this type of research have been playing an increasing role in the evaluation process. Their responsible attitude means that molecular biologists can no longer be seen as dreamers, naïve, irresponsible and potentially dangerous – the image that the movie industry has always been so keen to portray.

Research programmes using the methods of molecular biology started at the end of the 1970s. Their implementation was nothing short of a revolution. Within a few years the vast majority of laboratories involved in biomedical research were, at least to some extent, using recombinant DNA techniques.

The switch made by university researchers was particularly marked in America, where acceptance of genetic engineering was recognized as a prerequisite for obtaining federal research grants. More conventional fields of research were suddenly regarded by many as outmoded and destined for a slow death, although the scientists who resisted the pressure and stuck to their traditional ways of investigation – and succeeded – were later seen as heroes.

Molecular Biology: An Indispensable and Complementary Field

Today the enthusiasm initially generated by the promise of genetic engineering has been put into perspective and the scientific community has adopted a more balanced view, realizing that both types of scientific investigation, research using the traditional methods of biochemistry, physiology, organic chemistry and pharmacology, and molecular biology, are complementary. There are no longer sharp boundaries between the two approaches, and together their effect is to accelerate the rate of discoveries.

The 1988 Nobel Prize for Medicine and Physiology has underscored the new orientation. It was awarded to three scientists, Sir James W. Black, Gertrude B. Elion and George H. Hitchings, whose conventional research programmes since 1945 have led to the development of drugs which are among the most widely used today. Black participated in the discovery of beta-blockers, whose spectrum of application extends from myocardial infarction and arterial hypertension to the peripheral effects of anxiety and ulcers. He is also the inventor of cimetidine, which is particularly efficient against stomach ulcers. Elion and Hitchings led research projects which resulted in the elaboration of molecules preventing cellular growth, including pirimethamin, azathioprin, acyclovir and azydothymidin (AZT). These constitute drugs of choice for organ transplants and for the treatment of malaria, leukaemia, gout, AIDS and other viral infections – quite a number of applications!

Molecular biology is certainly bringing additional means to fight illnesses, but let us not forget the tremendous power of other methods which have made their mark and should never be considered out of date.

3

Genetic Markers and Evolution

DIVERSITY RULES THE UNIVERSE. FROM PHYSICAL, INERT MATTER TO living forms, from observable phenomena to elaborate thought processes, from ideas to tangible, manufactured products, heterogeneity and multiplicity are the hallmarks of anything we can think of. The very existence of life is characterized by genetic diversity. Billions of living species populate the earth, every one of them representing the manifestations of a cosmic blueprint. Whether the blueprint is predetermined or is unrolling before our eyes as time proceeds, it orchestrates the appearance and the development of all life forms through the selective pressure of evolution.

More extraordinary than the multitude of species in the world is the uniqueness of each member of any given species. Apart from biological twins, all human beings are different in all aspects of their physical and mental features. Thus blue eyes, brown hair, fair skin, short stature, a propensity to obesity, crooked nose and little feet are phenotypic expressions of genetic diversity. The same is true of behavioural traits, such as learning, memory, language and good or bad temper.

The first systematic studies of these variations have been carried out not on humans but on fruit flies, whose reproductive rate is so fast that genetic changes are quickly apparent. At first sight all fruit flies may appear alike, but they are not. Like all other living species, they display a remarkably wide spectrum of observable attributes, detailed investigations of which have helped us to lay down the foundations of modern genetics and to define the laws of genetic diversity.

What determines differences between species? We humans like to feel that we are superior to the rest of the living world. We can think, understand and build; we have control over the so-called 'lower' species. Maybe, then, our DNA molecules are longer than those from plants or animals. It is certainly true that a general trend exists whereby DNA length increases with biological complexity of organisms. The genome of a bacterium is 4.7 million base pairs long; that of a yeast, 15 million; that of a fruit fly, 155 million; that of a chicken, 1,000 million; and that of a human, about 3,000 million. However, there are many exceptions to this rule, and many other lower species possess longer DNA molecules than do humans. The DNA molecule of a mouse is, as with humans, about 3,000 million base pairs long, while the length of corn DNA is 5,000 million and that of a salamander or a lily flower, 90,000 million. These exceptions constitute what is called the C-value paradox, and they indicate that DNA length is not directly related to complexity of organism. Phenotypic diversity is actually the result of genetic variations.

We Are All Mutants

If we compare the DNAs from different individuals of a given species, we discover an intriguing fact: there are differences between individual DNA molecules. We now know that there are about 10 million of them in human DNA, and they seem to be randomly distributed all along the molecule. These differences can be the result of mutations (replacement of one nucleotide by another), deletions or insertions of one or more nucleotide, or rearrangements (displacement and reorganization) of short DNA sequences; most are mutations. These variations, which can be likened to checkmarks all along the DNA chain, are called 'genetic markers'.

DNA sequence variations arise through a variety of mechanisms. Many chemicals, ionizing radiations such as X-rays and UV radiations are mutagens (they can cause mutations). DNA replication is itself a very critical process. During mitosis and meiosis, each DNA strand from the mother cell serves as a template for new complementary strands, so that the resulting cells (two after mitosis and four after meiosis) contain duplicates of the mother cell DNA molecule.

DNA replication is performed by a combination of DNA poly-merase, an enzyme which copies DNA strands, and several repair enzymes. The function of repair enzymes is to correct mistakes introduced during the manufacturing of the new DNA strands. Even so, errors are still sometimes made, and this is the basis of evolution. One nucleotide is replaced by another type – it can also be added or deleted in the DNA chain – and in short, a mutation is created. DNA replication, however, constitutes a highly controlled, incredibly well-designed process, and the odds of a mutation at any given time are only one in a billion.

Mutations arising during mitosis are not transmitted in subsequent generations. Some of these mutations are silent (do not produce any effect). Others have drastic consequences: for example, we now know of mutations affecting genes implicated in the regulation of cell division. Cells with this modified DNA escape the action of control mechanisms and start to divide in an anachronous manner, which leads to out-of-control cell proliferation, otherwise known as cancer.

Mutations arising during meiosis, on the other hand, are transmitted to offspring according to the statistical laws of heredity: they form stable elements inherited in a Mendelian fashion. Meiosis is the time when genetic recombination occurs. DNA from matching chromosomes exchanges homologous genetic material in the process of crossing over. This event represents another source of possible DNA variation, such as modification of larger sequences due to the effect of non-homologous recombination. This event takes place because, before the actual exchange of DNA material, the pairing between the two chromosomes can be slightly shifted. Such a mismatch is perfectly understandable, in particular within regions consisting of DNA sequence repeats. These will then pair and exchange genetic material with a corresponding sequence on the other chromosome, which although complementary is not quite exactly homologous.

Other mechanisms for hereditary variations include chromosomal duplication, translocation (transfer of a DNA sequence from one chromosome to another), inversion of DNA fragments on a given chromosome, and gene jumping. DNA is not a static molecule, but represents a dynamic evolutionary system in which pieces move around, and minute as well as larger variations take place constantly.

Polymorphisms

Genetic variations all along the DNA molecule are also called genetic polymorphisms. As their name suggests, they confer various 'forms' to individual genetic material. Genetic polymorphisms, found all along the DNA molecule, have different effects according to their relative locations. When a variation occurs within the sequence of a gene, it can affect a codon in such a way that the resulting protein will have a change of one amino acid – a variant protein. A great number of variants, or polymorphic proteins, have been reported over the years. We knew of their existence before the responsible

DNA polymorphisms were found, because proteins were studied long before DNA. The amino acid change sometimes has little or no effect on the function of the protein. However, it can generate drastic alterations in chemical and physical properties of the variant protein.

This is the case in sickle cell anaemia, a very severe form of anaemia in which the red blood cells display a characteristic sickle shape when the haemoglobin is deoxygenated. Their inability to change shape inhibits their movement through small capillaries, where they can get stuck and thus prevent blood supply to the parts of the body these capillaries serve. Clinical manifestations range from fatigue to skin ulcerations and tissue necrosis (death due to lack of oxygen), all accompanied by severe pain. In this disease the culprit is a slight modification in the haemoglobin molecules, a single amino acid change caused by a single point mutation in a single gene.

Red blood cells provide the correct supply of oxygen to the various tissues of the organism and remove carbon dioxide from those tissues. This is accomplished by the haemoglobin contained in the red blood cells (the red colour of blood is due to the spectral properties of these haemoglobin molecules). A haemoglobin molecule is composed of four protein chains of two kinds (two alpha-chains and two beta-chains). The only, apparently very minor, difference between normal haemoglobin, or HbA, and sickle cell haemoglobin, HbS, concerns the sixth amino acid of the beta-chain (which is 146 amino acids long). At that position, a glutamic acid in HbA is replaced by a valine in HbS, and that is all. This unique amino acid change in one of the two chain types is the root cause of all the clinical symptoms of this terrible disease.

The change from glutamic acid to valine is caused by one nucleotide mutation in the sixth codon of the gene coding for haemoglobin's beta-chain. In the case of the HbA gene, it is constituted by the triplet GGA (coding for glutamic acid), while in the HbS gene, a G to T substitution transforms it into GTA, a codon for valine.

Sickle cell anaemia epitomizes a genetic disease due to a single gene disorder. The genetic abnormality, a G to T modification, always results in the full expression of the disease (we say that the abnormal gene is fully penetrant). The identification of the nucleotide substitution has allowed scientists to identify the last piece of the puzzle. They have clarified the pathway of the disease from its direct molecular cause at the level of the genetic material to the plethora of clinical manifestations. They have determined the intermediate steps between the cause and the clinical effect;

the abnormal protein (biochemical defect); the process by which the red blood cells function abnormally (physiological defect); and the changes in the appearance of both red blood cells and affected tissues, such as capillaries and skin (patho-physiological changes). Sickle cell anaemia, therefore, is taken as a model system for the study of other monogenic disorders.

Imperceptible Effects of Genetic Variations

Some genetic polymorphisms have a cause and effect relationship even though they do not result in a variant protein. A DNA variation can modify the regulatory regions of a gene, so that its expression is impaired or the transcribed mRNA is more unstable and produces fewer protein molecules. As a consequence, levels of the coded protein no longer fall within the range required for proper functioning. Sometimes this effect is so slight that it will go undetected, and a low protein concentration, for example, will be diagnosed as acceptable. Although this slight imbalance in the amount of protein produced will not have any immediately striking consequences, the cumulative effect over years or decades can ultimately result in the appearance of clinical symptoms.

This phenomenon may explain, for example, certain undetected mechanisms of atherosclerosis. Cholesterol circulating in the organism is sometimes not eliminated fast enough because of minute abnormalities in transport and clearance mechanisms. A large, and as yet unknown, number of molecules are involved in these processes and it is conceivable that one or more of them might be inadequately produced. The result is a slow and insidious accumulation of cholesterol in the arterial walls until one day the arteries are so obstructed that a blood clot is stopped at the obstruction, thus preventing adequate blood supply. When this happens in coronary arteries (arteries feeding the heart muscle), a heart attack follows.

Most variations in the DNA sequence seem to have no effect on the fate of the organism. They occur either within gene sequences but induce no amino acid change – such mutations are called silent mutations – or outside genes and regulatory sequences and seem to be of no consequence for the organism. However, they may have an effect that is yet to be determined. Certainly, if they have no effect at all, it would seem that a large part of the DNA molecule is constituted of sequences that have no apparent function. At the moment, we simply do not know whether this is so, but scientists who have a deterministic approach find it hard to believe that a large portion of the genetic material is useless; if it were, surely it would have been eliminated through the processes of evolution. Nature is indeed very energy-efficient and does not like wasting its resources.

From Genotype to Phenotype

With all its polymorphisms, the genetic material (genotype) is expressed into observable characteristics of the organism (the phenotype). A particular phenotype corresponds to each given genotype. The very existence of genetic polymorphisms explains why we are all roughly similar in appearance but all bear noticeable differences in physical traits, such as size, weight and eye, skin and hair colour, in character traits and in behavioural traits. In short, genetic polymorphisms are responsible for diversity, and in that role they make life interesting. It should be emphasized here that the estimated number of polymorphisms and gene differences between individuals from the same ethnic groups (Greek, Pygmy, Japanese or a Borneo tribe) is about identical (only slightly lower) to the number of differences between individuals from different populations. The idea of the superiority of one ethnic group over another on the basis of genetic differences is thus shown to be unfounded and absurd.

The effects of genetic polymorphisms on physical and character traits make some of us incompatible with each other. In genetics 'assortative mating' is the term used to describe the fact that humans (as well as many other species) are discriminating in their choice of mate; the opposite is 'random mating' (mating irrespective of the phenotype). The study of whether mating is assortative or random is more than just an intellectual exercise: there are major consequences for the transmission of hereditary traits. Indeed, assortative mating results in the transmission of genetic traits which are selected on the basis of the expressed phenotype.

Genetic Markers Form the Basis for Evolution

The existence of genetic markers provides further support for the theory of evolution, first codified by the British naturalist Charles Darwin in his treatise *The Origin of Species by Means of Natural Selection*, published in 1859. Because of genetic polymorphisms, the genetic material presents numerous individual variations. These modifications arise through a continuous process. The rate of reproduction is greater than the available food resources can tolerate, and the resulting struggle for life ends in the death of the weakest and survival of the fittest individuals. Some genetic variations will confer advantages and others, disadvantages. Survival operates through a process selecting for advantageous characteristics and this process is called 'natural selection'. Under a given set of environmental conditions, the genetic make-up of an individual results in a particular phenotype which must be adapted to the environment in order for the individual to survive. Most variations result in minute changes which are insufficient to give a marked advantage. Such a selective advantage appears only through the process of orthogenesis, a mode of concerted evolution pursued in the same direction during thousands of years. Thus orthogenesis rather than individual variation is the essential factor of biological progress. These are the main lines of the accepted theory of evolution. However, there is still a major controversy among biologists: are DNA variations the result of chance events, following the laws of probability, or do they obey a predetermined blueprint through some selective pressure exerted by underlying mechanisms of evolution?

It could very well be a mixture of both. Mutations appear to occur at random in the genome, while selection operates through the environment (the situation is aptly summarized by the title of Jacques Monod's useful book *Chance and Necessity*, 1970). However, mutations do not necessarily occur randomly, and one particular example of directed mutagenesis has been proved. In the human genome the succession of the two nucleotides C and G is observed less frequently than it should be if it were to occur at the statistically predicted rate, yet this CG dinucleotide is a hot spot for methylation. What does that mean? Along the DNA molecule certain cytosines (and not the three other bases) sometimes undergo a slight chemical modification, the addition of a methyl group. This methylation is thought to affect gene expression. Not all cytosines becomes methylated but only those which are followed in the DNA sequence by a guanine. Methyl-cytosines can in turn be the object of a second chemical modification, resulting in the removal of another chemical group called an amine. The significant point is that a deaminated methyl-cytosine is a thymine. Replacement of a C by a T happens quite frequently and it seems to escape DNA control and repair mechanisms. Therefore, the dinucleotide CG, the hot spot for methylation, is also a hot spot for mutation. Some scientists believe that this could very well be part of a mechanism which exerts pressure to increase the odds of mutations at specific locations. Others, defenders of the neutral theory, claim that chance alone is at play.

Experimental evidence is backing up the theories developed by molecular biologists to enrich our modern perception of the mechanisms of evolution. We know now that most individual DNA variations have very little to no cause and effect relationship with observable phenotypes. Therefore, they escape the control of natural selection. If this is the case, we need to admit the existence of a selective pressure exerted by the laws of molecular genetics. And according to the views of many scientists, not the fittest, but the luckiest individuals, survive throughout evolution.

Modifications in our conceptualization of evolutionary processes have led to flashy press articles bearing such evocative titles as 'Darwin's theory of evolution questioned' and even 'Collapse of Darwinism'. Let us not be as radical. Darwin's theory of evolution is the best overall model that we have so far to explain lineage relationships between living species populating the earth – or having populated it at one time or another. Naturally, in light of what DNA studies are yielding, some of the aspects of that theory – which was formulated in 1854 – want improvements while others need revisions.

Living Organisms in Space and Time

Molecular genetics is helping to evidence what we had suspected for some time already – the existence of genes that control the development of living organisms both in time and in space. Until now, very little has been gathered on hereditary material regulating the timely unfolding of developing, living, structures; knowledge in this domain only amounts to the demonstration of the existence of a cell's molecular clock. On the other hand, data on spacial development has emerged, once again, from investigations on the fruit fly *Drosophila*.

Scientists have discovered, in the genome of the fruit fly, the presence of homeotic genes that control the execution of the blueprint dictating development and differentiation, and therefore that play a fundamental role in the design of the architecture of the animal.

Proper functioning of these genes ensures that legs, wings, head and abdomen develop at the right place and in correct proportions. Whenever these genes are affected – and this can be induced in laboratory conditions – anything can go wrong. An eye develops on top of the head or a wing grows from the abdomen.

Scientists have also observed in all homeotic genes of the fruit fly the presence of a small DNA sequence – the homeobox. They later found homeobox sequences in the genome of all animals, including humans. In higher organisms, we suspect that the organization of architect genes is of greater complexity, but investigations along this line of research will soon tell us why and how eyes, nose, mouth and ears appear at their right place on the face, feet exist at the end of the legs, and a human baby resembles a human adult rather than a monkey or a frog.

At the Frontier of Species

Questions about development of organisms and variations at the level of genetic materials lead to a more fundamental interrogation. If DNA has the same chemical structure in all living species, why can't different species breed? Why can't we observe centaurs – chimeras between horses and humans? The answer is contained within the two following definitions of a species. A species is constituted by a population of individuals who can breed and give birth, under natural conditions, to fertile offspring. A species can also be viewed as a population whose individuals can exchange their genes.

Three barriers prevent breeding across different species – a geographical, an anatomical and the most insurmountable of all, a genetic barrier erected at the molecular level. Indeed, genetic texts in separate species are incompatible, as if they were actually written in different languages that have no common point and cannot combine. Although we are not yet able to decipher the phenomenon underlying this interpretation, we suspect that the key to its explanation is somehow hidden within the junk DNA part of the genome. A difference of 15 to 20% separates genetic materials from different species. Yet, and this has attracted much publicity, comparison of human and chimpanzee DNAs indicates a 1% difference. This result applies in fact to common genes that have been studied. Genes, however, make up only 3% of the total length of the genome of higher organisms, while intergenic sequences – the junk DNA – fills the remaining 97%. Now, an overall comparison of human and chimpanzee DNAs, taking into account all intra- and inter-genic regions, does reveal a global difference of 15 to 20%.

Integrity of genetic materials is preserved by a system of enzymes responsible for proof-reading and correcting mistakes made by the enzymatic machinery whose role is to copy DNA molecules before cell division (DNA variations are generated by the tiny amount of errors that remain uncorrected). By inactivating such corrective systems, scientists have been able to create within the brief time of a laboratory experiment, a new bacterium species from two species which had diverged from a common ancestor over a period of 150 million years. After neutralizing the correctors of *Salmonella typhimurium* and *Escherichia coli*, they succeeded in making a chimera that they named *Salmorichia*. Similar experiments on higher animals would be technically more difficult to realize. For the moment, they remain prohibited.

Genetic-Marker Technology

Genetic markers, then, are DNA variations due to mutations (nucleotide changes) and to deletions, additions and rearrangements of nucleotide sequences. They differentiate individual genetic materials. Identification of these markers is something else that has been made possible by molecular genetics.

The detection of genetic markers involves the use of restriction endonucleases. As mentioned in Chapter 2, these are enzymes isolated from micro-organisms which cut DNA at precise nucleotide sequences – their restriction sites. They are usually compared to molecular scissors which can be used to cut a DNA molecule into fragments of the desired length. Scientists have at their disposal a battery of more than 150 restriction enzymes commercially available, and all of these recognize their own unique signature sequence. For example, the restriction endonuclease EcoRI, isolated from the bacterium *Escherichia coli*, cuts DNA each time it recognizes the sequence GAATTC. If a mutation modifies this restriction site into, say, CAATTC, GAAGTC or any other nucleotide permutation, the new sequence is no longer an EcoRI site and the enzyme does not cut the DNA molecule at this location. Alternatively, a mutation can generate a new EcoRI site.

Scientists visualize DNA regions of interest with the help of 'DNA hybridization'. The DNA sample is first submitted to the action of a restriction enzyme such as EcoRI, which cuts a human DNA molecule into about 1 million fragments of different lengths, ranging from a few to tens of thousands of base pairs. These fragments are then separated according to size through a molecular net by a technique of electrophoresis. The molecular net is composed of a gel made of agarose or polyacrylamide, hence the name 'DNA gel' to describe this stage of the experiment. Since DNA possesses an electrical charge, the migration of DNA fragments is realized by placing the size-separating gel into an electric field, where the electric force pulls the fragments from one end towards the other end of the gel. Smaller fragments migrate quite easily through the mesh, while larger fragments are retained; the larger the fragment, the more it is held back. So, at the end of the 'DNA run' the fragments have separated, the smaller to one end of the gel and larger to the other. However, the gel can be as small as a few centimetres long and is no more than a few tens of centimetres, so the DNA pattern in the gel, even though formed by 1 million fragments, seems like a smear. The trick is then to identify the precise DNA sequence being looked for. How can we detect a particular fragment of interest somewhere within this smear?

DNA-Hybridization Technology

The basis for DNA detection lies in the principle of complementarity between DNA strands. To find a particular sequence, scientists use a copy of this sequence, a DNA probe. This probe can be any DNA sequence (a gene or any part of it, a non-coding sequence, part or all of a cDNA, or a chemically synthesized DNA fragment). The probe is labelled with a substance which can be easily detected: radioactivity or a chemical inducing a change of colour. Hybridization between the probe and the matching genomic DNA sequence can be achieved only if these sequences are single-stranded. Both the genomic DNA fragments in the gel and the labelled probe are thus 'denatured' (the two strands of all DNA pieces are separated from each other). The probe is put in contact with the DNA pattern and hybridizes only with the corresponding DNA sequence of its size gradient. This hybridization step is carried out either directly on the DNA pattern in the gel or on the DNA pattern that has been first transferred from the gel on to a thin hybridization filter, a membrane which is easier to handle and to store. The specific nature of DNA complementarity means that only the particular fragment whose sequence matches that of the probe is detected. It is visualized on an X-ray film in the case of radioactive labelling and by the detection of a change of colour in the case of chemical labelling involving a colorimetric reaction. The whole process of detection of DNA fragments is referred to as 'DNA hybridization', 'blot hybridization' or 'Southern transfer' (the latter after its inventor, E. M. Southern, who reported his discovery in 1975).

RFLPs, Invaluable Tools

Where does this leave us with genetic markers? Nucleotide substitutions which either create or destroy a recognition site alter the distribution of fragment sizes. So do nucleotide insertions and deletions, and rearrangements of DNA sequences. For example, if the

DNA sequence constituting a probe corresponds to a genomic region located between two EcoRI restriction sites, the blot hybridization methodology of an individual genomic DNA cut with EcoRI will reveal one fragment. In another individual DNA in which a mutation has generated an additional EcoRI site between the two previous ones, two fragments are detected. On the other hand, if a variation destroys one of the two original EcoRI sites, only one fragment will be detected, but it will be larger in size, depending on the position of the next EcoRI site. These variations in the distribution of fragment patterns among individuals constitute what are called 'restriction fragment length polymorphisms' or RFLPs, commonly known as 'rifleps' or 'ruflups'.

Highly Polymorphic Markers

A marker must be highly variable in order to be useful. Unfortunately, this is not the case with most RFLPs, which result from either the presence or the absence of a restriction site: they are dimorphic rather than polymorphic. In molecular genetics the usefulness of a genetic marker is measured by a value called the polymorphic information content. For a single dimorphic site, this value is low and can be increased only by using additional RFLPs in a combination of dimorphic sites. Another approach is to have a true polymorphic marker with a highly variable pattern. Alec Jeffreys and his research team in Leicester have solved this problem with the discovery of minisatellites, which are composed of repeats of a core sequence about fifteen base pairs long. These repeated sequences, related to each other, are widely scattered throughout the DNA molecule. Jeffreys and his colleagues have identified several sets of minisatellites sharing similar or identical core sequences. In 1985 they designed a method to detect minisatellites using a probe derived from the sequence found in an unexpressed part (an intron) of the myoglobin gene – the gene coding for a muscle protein. This method was the basis of a test for genetic-identity testing which they called 'DNA fingerprinting'. This test was immediately used commercially by the giant UK pharmaceutical company ICI, and has revolutionized the field of identification of individual DNAs.

Minisatellites have undoubtedly filled a gap in genetic-marker technology. They can detect true polymorphisms, because there is a highly variable number of repeats at any particular location. Furthermore, as many as twenty different genomic locations can be examined at the same time, making results very informative. However, this extreme hypervariability results in the visualization of a DNA pattern of up to eighty bands that can be difficult to differentiate. The complexity of the observed patterns makes this technique most appropriate for the tracing of the transmission of markers within extended families, not for the identification of unrelated persons.

Scientists have searched and found additional markers of this kind. Some DNA regions are composed of a variable number of core sequences which occur at unique genetic locations rather than being scattered over up to twenty different regions. These are technically easier to handle, resulting in simpler patterns constituted by more intensely visible bands, and are thus easier to analyse. As a result of this practical advantage, they have gained wide acceptance in both scientific and non-scientific communities. For example, in America the FBI, which is closely involved with decisions in the field of forensic medicine, has voiced its preference for hypervariable, single-location probes.

RFLPs and the Map of the Human Genome

Why detect all these different RFLPs? One of the long-term goals of molecular genetics is to establish a complete map of the human genome. This map will be made up of genetic markers evenly spaced all along the DNA molecule. The distance between every two markers should ideally be such that they can give information on the whole DNA sequence that is between them. This way it will be easy to trace the fate of any given DNA sequence, even during the phenomena of genetic recombination – exchange of homologous sequences during the process of meiosis. We will then gain immediate access to any genome location, no matter where it is. The question is, how many markers are necessary to cover the whole genome? We do not know the exact number but, with the present state of our knowledge, assume that it could be in the vicinity of a few thousand.

Any attempt to calculate the precise number of markers necessary to build a complete map of the human genome involves many unknowns. How many good (informative) markers are there? Do these exist in all DNA regions? How much recombination occurs in all parts of the genome? And what distance do we want between consecutive markers? The last two questions are related, because the spacing between genetic markers should make it possible to follow the position of all DNA sequences, even after recombination.

All scientific fields have created their own units, the names of which tend to be a mystery to non-specialists. In classical genetics a unit of recombination is called a Morgan, after T. H. Morgan, the American geneticist and recipient of the 1933 Nobel Prize for Medicine. A Morgan represents a chromosomal length over which recombination can occur. To molecular geneticists this distance is so great that it is seldom used; they prefer instead the centiMorgan (one-hundredth of a Morgan). The actual number of DNA base pairs represented by 1 centiMorgan is variable. It is a function both of which chromosome and of which part of the chromosome we are talking about. On average, however, we can assume that one centiMorgan is equivalent to 1 million base pairs.

The elaboration of a map of the human genome represents an extraordinary project, yet several laboratories worldwide have been moving quite fast towards this goal. In the forefront are Ray White's laboratory at the Howard Hughes Institute of the University of Utah, Salt Lake City, and the company Collaborative Research of Amherst, Massachusetts. Today scientists have discovered a few thousand genetic markers. A selection of the most informative and appropriate of these has permitted the construction of a 5-centiMorgan linkage map (genetic markers roughly separated by an average of 5 million base pairs) covering a good 90 per cent of the whole human genome. But large gaps (corresponding to the remaining 10 per cent) remain. One aim of molecular geneticists within the next few years is an improvement in the resolution of the map. They hope to construct a linkage map in which high-quality genetic markers will be separated by distances of 1 centiMorgan. Only then will it be possible to probe all parts of the human genome efficiently.

Genetic and Physical Maps of the Human Genome

Molecular geneticists are in fact working on the elaboration of two types of map whose functions are complementary: a genetic linkage map and a physical map. A genetic-linkage map corresponds to the assignment of genes and gene loci of interest to particular chromosomes. The proximity between two loci is determined on the basis of their being transmitted together. A physical map, on the other hand, corresponds to the regular spacing of identifiable landmarks along the DNA molecule. While genetic distances are measured in centiMorgans, physical distances are measured in terms of observable chromosomal distance or directly in base pairs.

Banding patterns identified on chromosomes during karyotype determination constitute a rough physical map, because each observable band corresponds to millions of base pairs regularly spaced along the chromosomes. Molecular geneticists have created new tools to elaborate higher-resolution physical maps by cutting DNA molecules into very large fragments and reconstituting the original order of the corresponding fragments. Overlapping, continuous fragments of the genome are referred to as 'contigs'.

The development of two revolutionary techniques allows the separation and study of very large DNA fragments, up to 5 million base pairs long. The first, yeast artificial chromosome, permits the cloning of larger fragments. The second, pulsed field gel electrophoresis (PFGE), allows the separation of these very large fragments by electrophoresis.

Incomplete maps available today are thus constituted by contigs separated by gaps of various lengths. Obtaining a higher-resolution map involves piecing together the smaller and smaller contigs that cover the whole genome.

Practical Applications of Genetic Markers

Genetic markers thus constitute preferred tools in the identification of DNA from different individuals. They also allow the exploration of DNA sequences which surround them. This is why there are two main practical applications. The first, DNA identity testing (or genetic-identity testing, or DNA fingerprinting), is now routinely used in criminology, forensic examination and paternity testing to solve difficult cases. The second involves the development of diagnostic and prognostic tests for hereditary diseases.

Their direct use in medical practice apart, genetic markers help unravel the mysteries of DNA molecules. Answers to fundamental questions about evolution, the regulation of life's molecular mechanisms and the complexity of organization are within reach.

The Need for a High-Resolution Map of the Human Genome

Whether for genetic-identity testing, for identification of genes implicated in hereditary diseases or for understanding the functioning and evolution of genomes, we need to explore all the regions of the human DNA molecule. To this end, it is necessary to discover the largest number of genetic markers giving information on all the genes contained in the molecule. Such an extensive set of markers will provide more information for linkage analysis, will increase the likelihood of detecting diseased genes and will greatly facilitate both gene identification and gene cloning. A comprehensive study of the complete DNA molecule is part of what is called 'the human-genome project', whose significance is analysed in the next chapter.

4

Should We Sequence the Human Genome?

'A FANTASTIC PROJECT', 'THE BIOLOGICAL ENDEAVOUR OF THE TWENTY-first century', 'a ridiculous enterprise', 'nonsense' and 'a crazy idea' are phrases that have been used by journalists and scientists alike over the past few years in relation to the project of determining the sequence of the human genome. Why such contradictory views?

'Sequencing the human genome' could have been the title of a science-fiction movie only a few years ago; today it is a concrete reality. In the last fifteen years molecular biology has been instrumental in launching several revolutions, both in basic and in applied medical research. Today we are in a position to undertake the formidable task of sequencing systematically the human genome: that is, determining its chemical structure.

Value of the Sequencing Project

Although there is no consensus among scientists about the desirability of substantial and immediate investment of time and money in order to achieve this aim, there is probably no dispute about the importance of the information sought. Qualitatively, the project is on a par with our efforts to send humans to the moon twenty-five years ago. What we will reap from the sequencing enterprise is comparable to the knowledge to be gained in outer space or at the heart of subatomic particles. In this respect, the genome project covers territory located between the infinitely small world of particle physics and the infinitely large world of cosmology.

Compared to other super-projects, the sequencing of the human genome will not yield a unique, striking, phenomenal result to excite the public's curiosity. While the Manhattan project resulted in the explosion of the atomic bomb and the Apollo project led to Neil Armstrong's walking on the moon, there will be nothing of the sort when we have established the sequence of a human DNA molecule. Instead, it will be a starting-point, an open door to vast, uncharted territories. Only when we have reached this starting-point will we be able to begin trying to understand what is written in the sequence. As often pointed out, we may find ourselves in a position where the Book of Life is open before our eyes and we are unable to read it because we do not know the language.

Actual Meaning of Sequencing a Genome

What exactly is meant by 'sequencing the human genome'? Human hereditary material, the DNA molecule (generally observed in the form of chromosomes), is constituted by 3 billion units – the nucleotides – linked to each other in linear fashion. All the information necessary for life itself is contained in this linear chain of DNA – more precisely, in its specific nucleotide sequence. Hence, in order to understand how this DNA functions, we should determine the complete sequence of the DNA molecule. To understand the Book of Life, we must be able to read its 3 billion letters.

Sequencing the human genome is in fact part of broader research programmes aimed at determining genome sequences of other species as well. The intrinsic value of one type of sequence is very limited. Scientists can take full advantage of an established sequence only by comparing it with sequences of genomes from other species, in order to identify common and conserved regions, i.e., sequences which are found in the DNA of all species, as well as to pinpoint differences that can explain phenotypic variations. This is why many investigators feel that we should refer not to the 'human genome project' but to 'genome projects'.

Sequencing projects have triggered a renewed interest in the fundamental questions raised by molecular biology in general. The public rightly asks whether we should continue to manipulate the hereditary material of human beings or tamper with the DNA from any living organism, and whether the resulting discoveries will not be misused in some new form of eugenics.

Scientists have put forward four additional kinds of concern that are more pragmatic and directly concern the decision to engage in a massive sequencing effort. First, although experimental methods are available to carry out this endeavour, are they as efficient as they should and could be? Second, is the project scientifically worthwhile: that is, will the information obtained be commensurate with the amount of work and resources involved? Third, would laboratories involved in basic research run the risk of becoming sequencing factories – good science giving way to technological determinism? And fourth, would the money needed for a project on such a scale be more usefully spent maintaining activity in other areas of basic research?

Molecular biology is a field in which researchers not only question themselves but are also ready to reconsider their work. The amount of financial support for basic research is limited in all the advanced countries. Moreover, scientists are aware of the dangers of misused genetic information. They know that they should take full responsibility for the data generated, and that genetic information should be used only to improve the human condition. These concerns echo those discussed extensively at the Asilomar conference in 1975, and are regularly examined by the numerous commissions and committees that have convened over the past fifteen years.

Whose DNA?

Perhaps the most relevant basic question that has been asked over and over again from the very beginning is, 'Whose DNA?' Indeed, the human DNA molecule that will be mapped and sequenced is to serve as a reference for all subsequent comparisons. It is clear, however, that this first-established sequence will be the result of an amalgam of DNA pieces isolated from genomes from many different sources, depending on which laboratory has sequenced which fragment: the reference human genome will be a composite DNA molecule. This is unavoidable, because the project is already being conducted in many laboratories throughout the world. The work started before scientists could agree on complete worldwide collaboration and at the moment, even discounting rivalries between scientific teams, the logistics of such an exercise would be boggling.

An Inappropriate Question

The question of whether or not DNA should be sequenced is inappropriate. Molecular biologists isolate and study new genes almost every day and have been doing so for over twelve years now. As a routine part of their investigations, they seek to determine the sequences of the genes they work on (which is used to ensure fast data publication). As a general rule, scientists tend to sequence all the DNA fragments they isolate in their laboratories. If not, this is usually because of lack of time or because they are not yet equipped with the material to do so.

They seek to obtain sequence data not for the sake of sequencing every nucleotide they can put their hands on but to gain knowledge on the particular DNA fragment which is the object of their research. This allows comparison with other known DNA fragments in order to find sequence similarities and differences, which are useful in deciphering gene functioning and regulation, as well as understanding the utility of DNA regions which do not code for proteins.

There is no doubt that one day, little by little, piece by piece, the whole sequence of the human genome will be completely determined. That day, however, could be in a very distant future if the present, sporadic approach is maintained. Despite the large amount of work completed during the past decade, barely 1 per cent of the complete human DNA sequence had been determined by 1990.

The opinion of staunch advocates of the sequencing project has been unambiguous from the start. They cannot understand this slow progress, particularly since research laboratories already possess the techniques necessary to move much more quickly. They want to start giving continuous support to the project so that it can be carried out in as short a time as possible.

Major Undertakings Afoot

The American government initially decided to get started in a major way in the mid-1980s. Under the direction of the Department of Energy, sequencing divisions were created in two research centres, one located in Livermore, California, and the other in Los Alamos, New Mexico (where the atomic bomb was developed).

Government institutions were not alone in showing a marked interest in the enterprise. Nobel Prize winner Walter Gilbert, a Harvard University professor and former president of the Biogen company, originally planned to start a biotechnology company, Genome Corporation, working solely on sequencing the human genome. However, he soon dropped his idea. There are several reasons for this. The very concept of a company expecting to make money on such a project has always been rejected by both the public and scientists. First of all, a privately owned company is immediately synonymous with legal secrecy, which is ethically incompatible with the essence of such a project. Furthermore, there are practical obstacles. Starting a venture-capital company would require tens of millions of dollars, and while it might have been possible to raise that sort of money a few years back, when biotechnology was viewed as the miracle money-maker, today private investors are much more wary. As a consequence, several companies have folded, others have been bought by bigger pharmaceutical companies and of the ones that still remain, many are worth a fraction of what they were a few years ago.

Then again, scientific advisers have always been averse to the concept of a sequencing company. Technical difficulties apart, it has never been clear how such a company could reimburse the start-up money within a reasonable time, nor become commercially viable. The idea put forward was to charge money for access to all the sequence data entered in a central computer – a scheme which has always been considered as hazardous, to say the least.

Current Views

In view of the difficulties inherent in the sequencing project, international scientific opinion has reached a consensus over the past three years or so and at present nobody is seriously thinking about sequencing the human genome. What has triggered this change of attitude?

Scientists have simply realized that they were trying to move too fast and that maybe their research proposals were in advance of their real technical abilities. Advances in molecular biology may indeed be spectacular, but we should not attempt to move too far too soon. After detailed evaluation of the pros and cons, research decision-makers have agreed to modify their original intentions. At this stage, the project has entered a phase which may be best described as preparatory.

Jean Dausset, a Nobel Prize winner and the director of the Centre d'Études du Polymorphisme Humain (CEPH) in Paris, has stated: 'at this very moment, it would be wise not to start a blind and systematic sequencing, which would be both expensive and very slow. It is of the utmost importance, however, to prepare without any further hesitation the time when all suitable conditions will be ready.' (*Pour la science*, no. 135, January 1989.)

First Objective: A Preparatory Phase

What will this preparatory phase achieve? What preparations do we need to make? Today's efforts are concentrated in four major areas. First, development and improvement of the existing technologies used in molecular biology, and in particular of those specifically applied to DNA sequencing. Second, automation of all the experimental procedures. Third, elaboration of computer software directly adapted to the treatment and analysis of DNA sequences. And last but not least, intensification of the research on genetic markers.

In short, scientists have decided to prepare the ground for the time when it will be possible to sequence DNA on a massive scale with optimal efficiency. To that end, they will emphasize genetic-marker research while improving molecular biology methodologies.

The labour involved in carrying out the human-genome-sequencing project is not only gigantic; it is also extremely repetitive. Hence as many experimental procedures as possible must be automated in order to reduce the need for highly trained laboratory personnel. Automation will also serve another purpose. Today's research techniques applied in the most advanced research laboratories will be tomorrow's clinical laboratory procedures. Once genetic testing is performed routinely to the extent that has been predicted, reference laboratories will be able to execute the same tests over and over. Laboratories need to function under a law which can be summed up as 'reproducibility', and only a machine can achieve complete reproducibility when performing elaborate but routine tests.

As of 1989 two American companies (Applied Biosystems, San Carlos, California, and Dupont de Nemours, Wilmington, Delaware) had each introduced an automatic-sequencing machine on the market. These automatic sequencers are the first generation of what promises to be a long series as their capabilities are improved. Although at present they can sequence about 10,000 nucleotides per day, 1 million nucleotides would be a more desirable number if a massive sequencing programme was to be undertaken.

The other problem with these automatic sequencers is of a more general order. They perform only the actual sequencing step. All other experimental steps, from DNA isolation to computer-sequence analysis, are next in line for automation, and several companies are already working to fill this gap. Japanese scientists are moving ahead with their super-sequencer, a series of robotized equipment developed by consortia representing government and industry. Their original target, announced at the end of 1987, was to sequence 1 million bases per day. At the moment their capability lies in the range of 10,000 bases per day (matching that of the American machines) but their more realistic goal is to reach a figure of 100,000 bases within 'a few years'.

In Europe Amersham International (Amersham, England) is working as part of the European-based Eureka project on the automation of all laboratory techniques, including those of molecular biology and DNA sequencing.

Repetition occurs at all levels of the experimental chain of events.

Data entry in the computer system consists of typing endless sequences made up of combinations of four letters only, A, C, G and T – the four types of nucleotides comprising the DNA molecule. Many research centres have set up their own sequencing facilities. These consist of laboratories whose main function is to determine sequences of DNA fragments isolated by the various research teams. I have heard more than one scientific director in charge of such a facility admit that it is necessary to switch technicians at the computer keyboards after they have entered 100,000 nucleotides. Otherwise, they would go crazy! Here again, the solution is to automate data entry.

After its entry, the data needs to be analysed, and that step requires an extraordinary computer base. Printing the information contained in the human DNA molecule would fill 200 Manhattan telephone books or make up a pile of daily newspapers accumulated over a three-year period. Once nucleotide sequences have been typed in, the various DNA fragments have to be placed in the correct order so that the exact sequence found in the chromosomes can be reconstituted. The computer can then perform a number of operations on the global sequence. It should, among many other things, recognize sequence homologies; find gene locations; pinpoint eventual similarities in the gene arrangements; and perhaps also identify DNA segments, unknown as yet, which will give us some clues about genomic regulation and functioning. Although much progress has been made in this respect, no satisfactory software is available at the moment to treat DNA sequence data efficiently – a lacuna which will undoubtedly be filled in the near future! Nevertheless, the body of results already generated has yielded one surprising and interesting observation: genes coding for proteins with related functions are clustered together in the chromosomes to a greater extent than originally suspected.

The considerable technical progress made over the past two years has to some extent paved the way for the human-genome project. While the project would take 30,000 years if conducted manually, today's state-of-the-art technology has already reduced that to 3,000 man years.

Mapping: A Good Compromise for Sequencing

The idea of determining the sequence of the human genome has not been abandoned but the general view is that it should wait until such research, first, is warranted, second, can be done efficiently, and, third, is valid over other lines of research. Practically speaking, the original idea of the whole programme has turned into genetic and physical mapping, and sequencing of areas of medical interest. This has already resulted in the localization of over 1,500 genes out of the 100,000 contained in the human DNA molecule. Molecular biologists are moving extremely fast, but there is still a lot of work to do.

The research programmes delineated in this chapter are by no means limited to the study of the human genome. Its size, as well as the presence of repetitive elements and of regions that are known as 'unclonable', make that a very arduous task. These difficulties, together with technical limitations, probably mean that it will take as much time to complete the last 1 or 2 per cent as it takes to generate the first 98 or 99 per cent. This is why there is so much interest in smaller genomes from other species: they are easier to manipulate and serve as pilot projects. Apart from their intrinsic scientific value and their commercial applications, genomes from several other organisms constitute reality checks for testing technical novelties.

Let us consider *Escherichia coli*, for example. *E. coli* is a harmless bacterium, part of the flora living symbiotically in the human digestive tract and participating in digestion. (As an aside, this flora gets wiped out when we take oral antibiotics and so needs to be reconstituted. This process is helped by the ingestion of food containing micro-organisms – a good reason for eating yoghurt when on antibiotics.) Sequencing the genome of *E. coli*, which is about 800 times smaller than the human genome, is in itself a major undertaking. The project has already been started. In 1987 Charles Cantor's research team, working at Columbia University, New York, reported the first sketch of the *E. coli* genomic map, which they had pieced together as a puzzle constituted by twenty-three fragments – a preliminary task that had taken several researchers more than a year to complete. Efforts from at least two other independent laboratories have generated higher-resolution maps covering about 99 per cent of the total genome, leaving only a few gaps.

In fact, many simpler candidate genomes could be the object of initial sequencing efforts. Deciding which of them should be emphasized has been a subject of lengthy debates. In 1989 James Watson, in his capacity as director of the NIH Office of Human Genome Activities, suggested that some effort should be put into sequencing the hereditary material of the nematode *Caenorrhabdis*. The nematode, or flatworm, is a parasitic, thread-like worm whose genome, containing 100 million nucleotides, is the size of one single human chromosome. Why the nematode? The answer is that we understand its biology very well. We know that each animal is made up of 958 cells exactly, and each cell division has been described in great detail. It thus constitutes a model system for studying the biology of all living organisms. America and Britain are proposing to collaborate in a project to break down the nematode genome into 100 fragments with which to reconstitute the puzzle and obtain a physical map – a task requiring $600,000 a year. The actual sequence of all fragments would then be carried out by a team of fifty technicians over a period of six years.

There are many other organisms whose genetic material is under investigation. Among these we can mention micro-organisms such as yeast, plants such as rice, corn, barley, wheat and the weed *Arabidopsis*, scientifically important animals such as *Drosophila melanogaster* (the fruit fly) and the mouse, and economically valuable animals such as pigs and cows. Several laboratories are working on selecting genetic traits associated with higher milk production in cows and with increased meat production in beef. We are not talking here about hormone injections to obtain larger mass of poor-quality meat but about engineering larger animals with the highest-quality, naturally developing meat. The large number of genomes available for investigation leaves all laboratories with a lot of choices! The genome programme is thus not limited exclusively to the study of the human genome, and it makes a lot of sense to replace the restrictive terminology of 'human-genome project' with the shorter, more general but more appropriate designation 'genome projects'.

Commitments of Involved Countries

To a certain extent all countries are involved in some part of the genome enterprise. However, the size of their respective commitments varies. It is clear that America leads the way. The Department of Energy and the NIH spent $50 million on the human-genome project for the year 1989. They earmarked $130 million for 1990, and $300 million per year for fifteen years starting in 1995. Furthermore, the Department of Agriculture has recently appointed a plant-genome office and has submitted a proposal for $500 million to study plant genomes.

Britain has always been at the forefront of the genome project and has launched massive efforts in that direction. The Agriculture and Food Research Council has started a three-year programme costing

£14 million for investigations into plant molecular biology, and a consortium of five seed companies is funding studies to map wheat and barley genomes.

In France Jean Dausset plays a key role as director of the Centre d'Études du Polymorphisme Humain, a repository for genetic markers and for DNA obtained throughout the world from extended and clinically well-characterized families; it is also conducting a sustained effort to sequence the HLA system. In Italy Renato Dulbecco co-ordinates the task of sequencing the X chromosome. At the moment Germany is also planning several genome programmes.

A couple of years ago there was concern in America and Europe that Japan would soon take the lead in the human-genome project. Yet in reality this has not happened: Japanese research has remained confined to the development of automatic-sequencing machines. At the moment most of the funds are directed towards plant molecular biology: Japanese government and industry are currently spending $200 million on rice genetics and molecular biology. A human-genome programme would require a joint effort from at least three different ministries, but they are notorious for their rivalries. The situation will remain on hold for some time, because even if the various proposals were approved, it would take at least two years for the funds to be made available. Japanese molecular biologists had been hoping for a more modest sum in order to develop the computer software necessary to gain access to genome information available from other countries. The Science Council of the Ministry of Education, Science and Culture released, in 1989, a lump sum of $4 million for a two-year preparatory study, initially involving twenty researchers under the responsibility of Kenichi Matsubara of Osaka University. This money has been obtained from emergency funds that the Japanese government generally puts aside for research on earthquakes, which indicates that embarking on a human-genome programme is perceived as urgent after all!

It seems that every country wants a piece of the action. Alexander Bayev from the Soviet Academy of Sciences raised a fundamental question at a meeting in Valencia, Spain, in December 1988, as later reported in the monthly *Science*: 'The data [generated by the genome project] should not be the property or privilege of one nation, social group or private company.' At the end of 1988 the Soviet Union launched its own genome programmes on human, yeast, *Drosophila* and mouse DNAs.

Less developed nations have stated categorically that they want to be involved, although to what extent this is possible remains unclear at the moment. On the one hand, a representative from Chile proposed during the Valencia meeting that they could work on the hereditary diseases that are more prevalent in their respective countries. On the other, India is prepared to launch its own project to map the human genome, although a proposed figure of $200 million spread over fifteen years has been met with scepticism from investigators throughout the world, including India. Also, the need to import the necessary restriction enzymes and chemical reagents from elsewhere would exacerbate the problems.

Necessity of Worldwide Collaboration

The scale of the effort necessary for the genome project has underlined the need for collaboration between laboratories, whether these belong to the same or to different countries. We should try to minimize unnecessary duplication of data, although in scientific investigation, it is likely that the same experiments will be done in several places at the same time. This is a tricky area, because competition is a highly powerful motivating factor, forcing research teams to complete their projects as quickly as possible. It also helps to single out the best laboratories, the ones which are constantly the leaders in the race for discoveries.

However, the genome project represents too much time and money to let rivalries get in the way of efficiency. A project of such size, even in its preliminary phase, must be conducted in a collaborative manner. All laboratories involved in any part of the sequencing project, whatever definition we give it, need to communicate openly and co-ordinate their work. It is therefore of the utmost importance to disseminate all information quickly and freely. Efficiency means not only optimal methodologies but also co-operation among researchers.

These are precisely the goals of an international and independent association, the Human Genome Organization (HUGO). Founded in 1988, HUGO was started as a group of forty-two world-famous molecular biologists, among whom five (Renato Dulbecco, Jean Dausset, Walter Gilbert, François Jacob and James Watson) have been recipients of the Nobel Prize. Victor McKusik, from Johns Hopkins University, Baltimore, Maryland, was their first president (some members with a keen sense of humour suggested referring to the association as 'Victor's HUGO').

HUGO is an extra-governmental organization, but its existence will depend on both government and private funds. It will give research grants, organize scientific symposia and publish yearly reports on all material relating to genome mapping and sequencing. It will be a powerful information centre, gathering all kinds of data on DNA from all species. It also proposes to set up international centres whose function will be to determine the sequence of DNA fragments of known chromosomal origin which will have been isolated as part of genetic-marker and gene-mapping programmes.

If HUGO can accomplish its original goal to foster communication within the scientific community and between this community and the rest of society, a major obstacle will have been surmounted. Its success would undeniably trigger other operations of a similar kind. We can only encourage such initiatives and wish them the best of luck.

Concrete results, however, may be slower in coming than originally hoped for. At the end of 1989 little progress had been made towards raising the several million dollars that were needed. In order to enhance the political clout of the organization, Walter Bodmer, director of research at the Imperial Cancer Research Fund in Britain, was elected in December 1989 as HUGO's new president, replacing Victor McKusik.

Trends for the Near Future

The positive attitude of scientists involved in the genome enterprise has triggered worldwide collaboration. The European Community, for example, is pursuing a six-year, $20 million programme involving thirty-five laboratories and aiming to sequence the yeast's chromosome 3, while a US – Japanese effort is concentrating on yeast chromosome 6. Other European programmes have been proposed, but some remain at the discussion stage because several organizations – most active among them the German 'Greens' – have called for closer evaluation. Meanwhile, even UNESCO has announced its desire to be involved, and may very well begin by funding associations such as HUGO.

To conclude, these research programmes to sequence the human genome have enormous implications, both for the well-being of individuals and for the world's economy. The controversies raised have once again forced scientists to look at the value of their research programmes. Conceptual problems have fostered discussions, which in turn have led to the reaching of reasonable decisions. Researchers know they have to be very cautious and not waste funds. Since money is limited, they have agreed to shift emphasis away from basic, fundamental research and towards shorter-term programmes with a view to improving the human condition. As a result of this we can expect to see developments which will greatly benefit the scientific and medical communities.

5

Genetic-Identity Papers

WHILE I WAS SPENDING A FEW DAYS IN OLD AMERSHAM, IN MARCH 1989, I read in the local newspaper about a horrific murder that had shaken the whole community less than two years before. The brutality of the story contrasted strangely with the loveliness of the surrounding countryside.

The corpse of teenager Rachel Partridge, naked apart from a pair of socks, had been discovered in a barn near the village of Bledlow Ridge. Her attacker had broken her jaw, battered and raped her before strangling her to death. At the scene of the crime the police found tyre marks and a human footprint. In Rachel's hair they noticed the presence of small fragments of a rare type of insulation foam. Four weeks later these clues led to the identification of a prime suspect: Ronald Cheshire, aged thirty-one, the son of a respected, retired policeman. Ronald's van tyres matched the tracks observed near the barn, his shoe size corresponded to the footprint and in the back of his van was a whole block of the same insulation foam.

Despite this incriminating evidence, Cheshire kept proclaiming his innocence. It was his DNA fingerprint that finally gave irrefutable proof of his guilt. He had probably never heard of the technique of DNA identity testing used in criminal and forensic examination. In fact, this was one of the first cases in which Scotland Yard used it, and Cheshire may have wondered why a nurse took a sample of his blood when he was asked, together with 800 other men, to report to the police station. What he could not know was that the murderer's genetic identity card had been determined from DNA taken from the semen in Rachel's body. The results of the 800 tests were unambiguous: Ronald Cheshire's DNA fingerprint (ascertained from his blood sample's DNA) corresponded exactly to the murderer's fingerprint. This could mean only one thing – he was the murderer.

The newspaper report stated that '... his [Ronald Cheshire's] blood matched the semen found in the dead girl's body.' This, of course, is not strictly true. What should have been reported was that DNA molecules isolated from the semen specimen and from Cheshire's blood sample were identical, and could belong only to the same person. The fact is that two individuals cannot have the same DNA molecules; this is why a DNA test is so clear-cut and precise.

Methods for Determination of an Individual's Identity

Each human being possesses in his or her DNA molecule an individual, unique set of genetic markers. This set is like a personalized identity card written into the individual's hereditary material. The detection of these markers constitutes an infallible identification test in situations requiring paternity determination as well as forensic and criminal examination.

These fields, involving both medicine and the law, were already the objects of study before the advent of genetic markers. Scientists had developed a battery of methods based on the observation of bone and tooth structures, and of fingerprints. Up to 1985, before the advent of DNA fingerprinting, laboratories also had at their disposal a selection of more widely applicable techniques using biochemical markers such as protein polymorphisms (ABO blood groups and HLA markers), serum proteins and red blood cell enzymes.

However, tests using these biochemical markers are based on the principle of exclusion rather than positive identification: a suspect can be cleared but the culprit cannot be identified. The exclusion probability reaches 98 to 99 per cent in the best of all cases, so a maximum of 98 to 99 innocent people out of 100 can be safely assumed to be not guilty. With genetic markers, on the other hand, we are no longer talking about exclusion based on a given probability. Laboratories can positively identify an individual, and the margin of error is extremely low: in theory, the odds for making a mistake are, at the most, one in a million.

Unlike a passport or any kind of identity paper, a DNA molecule cannot be copied. Unlike fingerprints, which can be erased by filing fingertips, DNA cannot be altered. Genetic material is found in all tissues of the body, such as blood, skin, flesh, hair, brain and sperm. Since minute DNA amounts are required to perform these tests, very small tissue samples are sufficient. Even so, it often happens that the sample size is too small to be subjected to analysis. This technical difficulty has been overcome by molecular biologists, who have invented the method of polymerase chain reaction, which makes it possible to replicate any particular DNA sequence thousands of times. The combination of genetic-marker analysis and polymerase chain reaction is powerful indeed: genetic tests have been performed on DNA samples isolated from single hairs.

It is true that heat and UV exposure degrade DNA, and that micro-organisms can contaminate forensic samples with their own genetic material, yet forensic laboratories have been able to establish unambiguously DNA fingerprints from four-year-old samples. Molecular biologists have even been able to study DNA specimens extracted from animals frozen in permafrost for thousands of years, such as a 35,000-year-old bison from Alaska. The oldest human DNA samples were obtained from 8,000-year-old skeletons with well-preserved brains excavated by archaeologists in marshes in Florida. Scientists have also taken DNA from Egyptian mummies and from an extinct animal called the quagga.

In the case of paternity determination, which is also based on genetic-marker analysis, DNA sampling is naturally not a limiting factor. These tests are routinely carried out on DNA extracted from the white cells isolated from average blood samples.

DNA Fingerprints in Immigration Cases

Private and public laboratories are now routinely using genetic-identity tests, which are playing an increasingly important role in the legal field. The first case that was submitted to Alec Jeffreys and his colleagues in Leicester, shortly after publication of their DNA-fingerprinting results in 1985, concerned the need to establish proof of family relationship in an immigration dispute.

A boy of Ghanaian origin who was born in Britain had decided to go back to Ghana to live with his father. Later he changed his mind and wanted to come back to his mother in England. Immigration officials suspected a fraud, being convinced that the returning boy was a different child seeking residence in Britain. They called for identity testing, using the conventional method of biochemical markers, which failed to provide a definitive answer. Despite a small number of relatives available for testing, Jeffreys' method then proved 'beyond any reasonable doubt' that the child was indeed the mother's son. He was granted permission to return as a UK resident.

There have been many cases solved since then by DNA analysis, both in Britain and in America. Depending on which laboratory performs the analysis, these methods are based on Jeffreys' minisatellite technique, or the use of probes detecting hypervariable regions at a single location or any combination of probes identifying RFLPs.

Proof for Acquittal

DNA fingerprints can determine the identity of criminals, and they can also prevent miscarriages of justice. In Leicestershire, DNA fingerprinting was applied in a case involving the rape and murder of two teenage girls. Routine police investigations determined that the criminal's age was less than thirty. At first everything seemed to point to a seventeen-year-old. His DNA-banding pattern, however, did not match the one that had been obtained from semen left in the teenagers' bodies and he was acquitted. The court then called for genetic tests on all males in the county under thirty. Even so, it was by conventional methods of investigation that the murderer – a local baker who had managed to avoid the tests – was finally caught, charged and found guilty. The information generated by the massive DNA-screening tests was later destroyed.

Doubts on the Legal Validity of Genetic Tests

Tests for individual identification using genetic markers are undoubtedly sweeping the market in forensic medicine. Following in the footsteps of ICI in Britain, most of America's 300 forensic laboratories have announced that they are planning to implement DNA testing within the next two years. Under ideal experimental conditions, DNA fingerprinting constitutes the most accurate, precise and reliable technique for identification that we have developed. In America the leading commercial laboratories, Lifecodes Corporation (Valhalla, NY) and Cellmark Diagnostics (Germantown, MD), are so confident of the superiority of this new method that they have been ready to bet their future on its success.

In California, before they are released from prison, convicted sex offenders are required to give blood and saliva samples. These are kept aside in case it should be necessary to run tests quickly.

Having performed tests that have resulted in over 200 convictions, and a few acquittals as well, during the summer of 1989 DNA-testing laboratories met with their first major complication: experts in molecular genetics cast serious doubts over the validity of the procedures initially adopted. They were also suspicious of the claim that the rate of mistakes was between one in a million and one in a billion.

It begins to seem that a combination of three factors – first, an intangible faith in the principles behind these new-generation tests, second, the fact that only a few experts are fully aware of the technical limitations of genetic-marker technology, and, third, the prospect of commercial benefits – had precipitated the implementation of DNA fingerprinting in the field of forensic medicine. We may have moved a little bit too fast in making this technology available to the judicial system. As of 1989 there was in America no federal or state legislation to regulate DNA testing in private or public laboratories.

The root of the problem lies with decrees such as the US Frye Rule, which stipulates that a technique used in forensic medicine must be accepted by the scientific community and have gone beyond the experimental stage. Yet experimental procedures in DNA testing are still constantly being modified. As of 1989 there were no official guidelines to delineate what is called good laboratory practice in the applications of gene-marker technologies in identity testing. In short, it is quality control that has been questioned.

All of this hullabaloo was triggered by a twelve-week hearing in a New York court, which called for the help of respected molecular geneticists (including Eric Lander of the Whitehead Institute in New York) and ruled that Lifecodes' results in one particular case were unreliable. The case involved José Castro, who was suspected of stabbing to death his South Bronx apartment neighbour Vilma Ponce and her two-year-old daughter. Lifecodes was asked to perform a genetic-identity test on a DNA sample from a blood stain found on Castro's wristwatch. The answer was categorical: the DNA obtained from the forensic evidence was the same as Vilma Ponce's DNA. However, this opinion was later challenged on two grounds: lack of proper experimental controls and unacceptable size differences between two of the DNA pattern bands – differences that were dismissed by Lifecodes' scientists after 'subjective visual comparisons'.

Any scientist who has worked with genetic markers will understand me when I say that there are often technical difficulties in performing the experimental procedures of genetic-marker technology. Perfect reproducibility is extremely difficult to achieve, although automation will solve part of this problem. We all frequently observe not only shifts in DNA patterns but also the presence of additional bands of varying intensities which should not be there. Fortunately, we know the two major culprits: contamination with foreign DNA and degradation of the samples.

Such problems by no means cast doubt on the validity of these experiments – they are minor technical hitches common in all experimental scientific research. However, dealing with paternity testing and forensic evidence, data analysis should be submitted to more stringent criteria than 'subjective visual comparison'. The interpretation of results used in legal procedures can have a drastic impact on the lives of the people involved: rape sentences, murder convictions and large sums of money are at stake.

Naturally, José Castro's case triggered other legal challenges to the results of DNA fingerprinting. A preliminary hearing in Portland, Maine, at the end of 1989 set out again to determine whether DNA fingerprints are reliable enough for unambiguous evidence. Tests carried out by Lifecodes Corporation originally established that the DNA pattern obtained from the semen found on tissue from a sexually molested five-year-old girl matched the DNA extracted from the defendant's blood sample. The defence, however, later found out that a direct match was impossible because the different patterns had migrated differently. Lifecodes had used two non-polymorphic probes to determine the correction factor between the different experiments. One of these probes resulted in an exact match, while the other did not. This second piece of information was first hidden and then sent by mistake to the defence. After much debate, the prosecutor finally decided to drop his case. He also strongly criticized Lifecodes for its way of handling scientific data.

Rules to Govern the Use of Genetic Fingerprints

Points of contention for the use of DNA fingerprints in forensic medicine have generally included technical difficulties and other considerations stemming from assumptions taken for granted in human genetics. Moreover, the DNA from forensic samples is generally degraded and too small an amount for the laboratories to be able to run the controls necessary. All these points have to be taken into consideration. Precise sets of satisfactory guidelines to warrant certification of the methods were urgently needed and in 1989 forensic experts attempted to come up with a set of rules aimed at reaching agreement on technical standards, experimental protocols, the interpretation of results and the coding of data. These rules appear to be acceptable to scientists, lawyers and FBI forensic experts.

New York was the first state to go beyond the discussion stage and legislation came into effect in 1990. This has resulted in the constitution of a committee to check standards and determine the validity of DNA fingerprints prior to their use in court. The state will also accredit private laboratories. The federal organism best-suited to handle these matters, the National Academy of Sciences, was asked to carry out a fourteen-month programme on DNA technology in forensic medicine, with funds from such sources as the FBI, the NIH, the National Science Foundation, the National Institute of Justice and the Sloan Foundation.

One complication with the implementation of genetic-identity testing is that, as in any business, laboratories are reluctant to exchange freely technical information which is the basis for their success. The need is to reach a balance between secrecy over procedures and the sharing of information – not an easy task for companies that have risked their futures on DNA probes.

The controversy over the implementation of DNA fingerprinting teaches us a very important lesson: we must be extremely cautious when applying DNA technology to human matters. However confident we are in the value of these new techniques, we must take all the precautions necessary to prevent mistakes in their application.

Position of the UK

In the UK, the whole subject of forensic medicine is being put under questioning and there are calls for radical changes. This came especially after the heat that has followed the release of the Birmingham Six. In 1975 a bomb went off in a crowded pub in Birmingham, killing twenty-four people and injuring 120. Six Irishmen were arrested, convicted and imprisoned. In February 1991 they were released from prison on the grounds that forensic evidence presented at the trials had been inaccurate. (We now accept that both a chemical test and the more sophisticated technique of gas chromatography turn positive with products other than nitroglycerine such as, in particular, soap!)

In the light of this episode as well as of the problems encountered in some American courts with DNA fingerprinting, the general feeling is finally that the application of scientific methods to the detection of crime does not give absolute, clear-cut results. And many now advocate that forensic services should be run by public, non-profit-making, executive agencies at the service of the courts.

Mitochondrial DNA and Argentine Dictatorship

Tests for an individual's identification based on the use of genetic markers are most successfully applied when many family members are available for testing: the transmission of markers within the family can be traced with certainty. When only a few family members are available, the power of the test decreases, and it is sensible to carry out several tests in conjunction with other available methods, such as genetic fingerprints, blood groups, HLA typing, blood cell enzymes and plasma proteins. In some situations, however, even a combination of various methods does not give an unequivocal answer. This was the situation that scientists encountered in Argentina.

During the military dictatorship which prevailed from 1975 to 1983, over 9,000 people 'disappeared'. With the election of President Alfonsin, organizations such as Amnesty International started to exert pressure on the government to investigate the fate of these people. Among the 'disappeared' were children who had been taken away from their families, many of whom had been sold for adoption and are still alive today. One association which somehow received wide media attention was formed by grandmothers who were determined to recover their grandchildren. This was no easy task, because records have been erased and small children change a lot physically, as well as forget early childhood memories (although obviously fragments of some memories remain deeply hard-wired). Also, in many cases the parents, brothers and sisters of these children were shown to have been killed. Molecular genetics has generated another method to circumvent the lack of close relatives.

At the request of the government of Argentina, the American Association for the Advancement of Science (AAAS) chose Marie-Claire King, an epidemiologist from the University of California, Berkeley, to work on the problem, in collaboration with Anna-Maria di Lonardo of the Immunology Laboratory in Buenos Aires. Marie-Claire King and her teams have used another method invented by molecular geneticists. It has just one precondition: the existence of maternal relatives available for testing, even if they are quite distant. Why only relatives from the mother's side? Because the method is based on the detection of mitochondrial genes.

Mitochondria are intracellular organelles found in all cells of the body (except red blood cells), in which they function as power plants:

they are in charge of fulfilling the energy requirements of the cell. The number of mitochondria within each cell ranges from a few dozen to several thousand, depending on the tissue of the organism. Thus the cells of a muscle in activity, because they require a lot of energy, contain a very large number of mitochondria.

Mitochondria are similar in shape and size to bacteria. They also contain their own genetic material – a DNA molecule – which makes them amenable to investigation with the tools of molecular genetics. Their mode of transmission makes them useful in the determination of parental relationship: they are autonomous structures whose replication is independent of the cell's division process, and they multiply only by mitosis (i.e., by splitting in two). If we observe germ cells, we notice that ova (female germ cells) are full of mitochondria, because they contain all the energy requirement of the future embryo, while there are almost no mitochondria in spermatozoa (male germ cells).

After fecundation, the embryo's DNA is a random mixture of genes, half inherited from the mother and half from the father. Yet all of the embryo's mitochondria are exact copies of the mother's only. By the same token, they are also duplicates of the mitochondria of all relatives from the mother's side of the family.

As an aside, mitochondrial DNA does not have the same repair mechanisms as genomic DNA and is therefore more prone to mutation – in fact, the mutation rate in mitochondrial DNA is about ten times higher than in genomic DNA. Mitochondrial DNA is thus an appropriate material with which to study the processes of evolution, and molecular geneticists have long realized the value of its investigation. Sequence data obtained from 140 individuals all over the world have allowed evolution geneticists to propose that the first human being probably lived in Africa 200,000 years ago, not 1 million years ago, as advocated by anthropologists. All methods of investigation have their flaws, and thus the considerable time difference for the appearance of the first *Homo sapiens* is still much debated.

Back to identity testing. The method for identification of relatives from the maternal side of a family is conceptually simple. It involves studying their mitochondrial genetic markers, or establishing some mitochondrial DNA sequence, enough to prove that the mitochondrial DNAs under consideration are identical. Its application has been successful in Argentina, where more than fifty out of the 200 children ready for testing had been positively identified by the summer of 1989 and safely returned to their biological families – or what was left of them.

Many had worried that the transfer of adopted children back to their biological families would be traumatic, both because of the length of separation and also because of the moral values of the adoptive families (most of them had been military, from the time of dictatorship). The past few years, however, have calmed these fears. The children seem to have returned home without disturbing emotional side effects.

Diagnosis of Hereditary Diseases

THE SHORES OF LAKE MARACAIBO, VENEZUELA, SOUTH AMERICA. visitors passing by the little fishing villages had long noticed, without paying much attention to it, the apparently strange behaviour of some locals. They were seen zigzagging from side to side of streets and pathways, with expansive and uncontrollable movements, groping for objects while their minds seemed elsewhere. In these far and foreign countries, stranger things are known to happen, and there was little doubt in the visitors' minds that the culprit for this erratic behaviour here, as in many other countries, was alcohol.

In the early 1970s, however, a doctor from a military base decided to take a second look at the residents of the fishing villages. After careful examination, he identified the cause of the villagers' conduct. It was not, as everyone thought, alcohol, but a lethal genetic disease first labelled 'Huntington's chorea' and now known as Huntington's disease (HD). This is a rare inherited disease whose symptoms appear at the age of thirty-five, and sometimes even later. It starts with signs of depression and other psychiatric troubles, followed by loss of muscle control. Jerky motions precede severe, progressive dementia, and death ensues. The disease is an irreversible degeneration of nerve cells and unfortunately there is no treatment for it.

Over the years doctors presented case reports about the manifestations of the disease and demonstrated the clear-cut mode of inheritance. HD is an autosomal-dominant disorder, which means that men and women are equally affected and that a person who inherits the trait in his or her genetic make-up will inevitably be affected by the disease. It also means that children who have one affected parent have a 50 per cent chance of being affected themselves.

In 1979 the NIH appointed Nancy Wexler to conduct a thorough research programme on HD. On top of her research interests, she had a very personal reason to carry out studies on this disease: her mother had died from it. Nancy Wexler started by doing what every geneticist has to do when investigating an inherited disease. She compiled multigeneration pedigrees. On paper men are represented by a square and women by a circle, and relatives are linked by straight lines. She thus obtained pedigrees from 7,000 family members from the region of Lake Maracaibo, some of whom are affected with HD and others of whom are not. The complete diagram that she has drawn over the years covers about 100 feet on the walls of a corridor by her office at Columbia University.

Since 1981 research teams have gone yearly to the shores of Lake Maracaibo. Besides clinical data and presentations, they have also collected blood samples from over 1,500 volunteers. In 1982 the team of James Gusella from Harvard University joined in to carry out genetic-marker studies in order to locate the gene responsible for HD. Trying to find a single unknown gene within the 3 billion nucleotides of the human gene was like looking for a needle in a haystack. Since HD is inherited as an autosomal trait, however, they could at least rule out sex (X and Y) chromosomes, which decreased the size of the haystack a bit. Still, they were ready to try hundreds of DNA probes scattered all over the human genome to identify the one that would indicate the vicinity of the gene responsible for HD.

They did not have to expend that much effort, because the twelfth probe they used was the good one. They discovered that HD is due to an abnormal gene located on chromosome 4, and they could isolate other DNA probes in this chromosomal region which allowed them to develop a DNA test to diagnose HD. Eight years later, however, the causative gene has still not been identified. This may seem a paradoxical situation: we do not know the cause of HD, we do not know what triggers its onset, we do not have any form of treatment and yet we do possess a diagnostic test for that disease!

Molecular geneticists have completely solved the puzzle of many inherited diseases, Duchenne muscular dystrophy (DMD) and cystic fibrosis (CF) among them. DMD affects one male infant in 3,500. It is characterized by muscle wasting, which begins in early childhood, and death occurs before the age of twenty. Researchers know that, as with haemophilia, it strikes only boys, because the faulty gene is carried by the X chromosome. Once the rough chromosomed X region containing the DMD gene had been localized, researchers succeeded in identifying the DMD gene itself, which happens to be the largest one found to date (it is 2 million base pairs long and encodes a very large protein that has been called 'dystrophin'). This project represented a massive collaborative effort: one single article published in the journal *Nature* was signed by seventy-seven authors from twenty-four research centres located in eight different countries! CF, another inherited infection, is a devastating childhood disease caused by the impaired function of mucus-producing glands in the organism. In 1987 the CF gene was found to be located on chromosome 7, and by 1988 it was isolated and characterized. Thus not only are DNA tests available for diagnosis of both DMD and CF, but we have also now discovered the proteins whose abnormalities cause these diseases. The problem at this stage lies in the development of efficient forms of treatment for these problems.

Genetic Variations, Genetic Diseases and Genetic Markers

The comparison of human DNA molecules reveals the presence of up to 10 million variations between different molecules. Some of these DNA variations have drastic consequences for the production, the structure and the function of the protein coded by the corresponding gene. Many single DNA mutations result in severe or fatal diseases; so do larger DNA sequence modifications. Since these defects are written in the genetic material, they get transmitted to the offspring and constitute what are referred to as 'genetic diseases'.

Genetic-marker technology constitutes a powerful means to detect variations in individual DNA molecules; as such, it is the best tool for diagnosing genetic diseases. Since the genetic material remains unchanged during the whole life span of an individual (starting from the time of conception), genetic-marker technology represents the best method for prenatal diagnosis of inherited disorders.

Genetic Test for Sickle Cell Anaemia

The most celebrated example is also the first genetic disease whose causative DNA variation has been proven to exist: sickle cell anaemia, the particular form of severe anaemia where red blood cells lose their plasticity and adopt a sickle shape. As already mentioned, the culprit is the substitution of the sixth amino acid of the beta-chain of the haemoglobin molecule (at this particular location, the amino acid glutamic acid in the 'normal' haemoglobin's beta-chain is replaced by a valine). DNA sequence comparison has revealed that this substitution is due to a single-point mutation in the gene coding for the haemoglobin beta-chain where the nucleotide G is replaced by a T. The partial sequence at this location reads GGAGTCC in the normal gene (GGA is the codon for glutamic acid) and GTAGTCC in the gene causing sickle cell anaemia (GTA is a codon for valine). This G to T substitution in one of the two genes coding for human haemoglobin (the beta-chain gene, whose overall length is about 2,000 base pairs) is the unique difference which causes sickle cell anaemia. What a fine line indeed between health and disease, starting at the DNA level.

As luck would have it for molecular biologists, this DNA mutation affects the recognition site of several restriction enzymes, making it amenable to RFLP analysis. The most commonly used enzyme has been MstII, whose recognition sequence is GGAGTTC (partial sequence of the normal beta-chain). Upon the hybridization of a DNA sample isolated from a 'normal' individual, part or all of the beta-globin gene or DNA used as a DNA probe detects two fragments whose lengths are 1,300 and 1,100 base pairs. The mutation causing sickle cell anaemia results in the partial beta-globin gene sequence GTAGTTC, which is no longer the MstII signature sequence. Since this particular MstII site is destroyed, DNA blot hybridization results in the detection of a single fragment which is now 2,400 base pairs long (1,300 1,100). This RFLP analysis of DNA samples using a beta-globin DNA probe constitutes a diagnostic test for the detection of sickle cell anaemia.

There is a faster, easier and cheaper method to diagnose sickle cell anaemia in adults. It is based on the migration of the haemoglobin molecules themselves (and not of DNA fragments). In a size-separating molecular net placed into an electric field, normal haemoglobin does not migrate as fast as a 'sickle cell' molecule, because the change from a glutamic acid to a valine results in the disappearance of one electric charge. This well-standardized method has been in use in all clinical laboratories around the world for years, and the detection of sickle cell anaemia using DNA technology is no improvement over it as a diagnostic tool. It has, however, permitted the identification of the real cause imprinted in the hereditary material and provided the final proof that sickle cell anaemia is a genetic disease. It has opened the way for similar studies of all other hereditary diseases, and for the first time it gives physicians a precise, reliable and low-risk technique for prenatal diagnosis.

Extraordinary Frequency of Genetic or Inherited Diseases

About 3,500 genetic diseases have been reported to date. The effects of the observed symptoms vary greatly, from minimal to fatal. Over 1 per cent of newborn babies are affected by well-characterized genetic diseases, which also account for over 30 per cent of infant mortality in industrialized countries. One of the aims of molecular geneticists is to understand all these diseases. The first step remains the discovery of the underlying DNA abnormalities, a puzzle that DNA technology is helping to solve in an unprecedented way. Scientists are confident of the future and look forward to a day when these diseases will be efficiently treated and even cured.

The genetic material can be affected by two types of defects: the first results from gross chromosomal aberrations; the second, from minute variations such as mutations at the DNA level. Clinical syndromes due to chromosome abnormalities have long been recognized and described in great detail. They arise during the process of cell division, when chromosomes are copied and shuffled around, and during fertilization. Chromosomes are typically observed in a standard arrangement known as a karyotype. To obtain a karyotype, body cells are grown *in vitro* until they reach a stage of division at which the chromosomes are particularly well individualized and easy to stain with chemical dyes. Geneticists take a photograph through a high-power microscope, cut out the picture of the individual chromosomes and arrange them in homologous pairs. This karyotype allows for easy counting and observation of all the chromosomes. It has been shown that one in 200 babies presents a chromosome abnormality but the overall frequency is much higher and could account for 50 per cent of spontaneous abortions (miscarriages), because many of these anomalies are lethal.

All possible aberrations have been observed over the years: gain or loss of one or more chromosomes, broken chromosomes, deletions (loss of segments of variable lengths) and translocations (exchange of segments between chromosomes). Two of the many syndromes resulting from chromosome abnormalities are Down's Syndrome, due to trisomy 21 (presence of three chromosomes in the genotype instead of two), and the Philadelphia chromosome, an acquired abnormality associated with a form of leukaemia (chronic mycloid leukaemia) due to the translocation of the long arm of chromosome 22 to chromosome 9.

Most of the 3,500 reported genetic diseases are caused by the transmission of very precise DNA defects, as in the case of sickle cell anaemia. Since these are due to mutations of single nucleotides, or to abnormalities of short DNA sequences (a few to a few thousand base pairs), they cannot be detected with a karyotype. They can be identified only with the tools developed by molecular biologists, the most useful here being RFLP analysis, blot hybridization and polymerase chain reaction.

The classification of inherited disorders is based on their mode of inheritance. The two larger groups are composed of diseases whose mode of transmission is either unifactorial or multifactorial.

Unifactorial, Monogenic Diseases

The mode of transmission of all unifactorial (also called single-gene or monogenic) defects was precisely established long before genes were discovered. It follows what are known as Mendel's Laws. Gregor Mendel (1822–84), an Austrian monk and botanist who carried out experiments on plant heredity, is especially remembered for his experiments on the crossing of common garden peas, carried out between 1856 and 1866 in the gardens of a monastery located in the city of Brno, now in Czechoslovakia. His investigations allowed him to codify the transmission of unifactorial characteristics in the form of laws. The results, published in 1866, constitute the basis for the chromosomal theory of heredity, and so Mendel is considered to be the founder of genetics. As an anecdotal parenthesis, his work remained unknown during his lifetime and was rediscovered only at the beginning of the twentieth century.

DNA variations causing monogenic genetic diseases can be present on any human chromosome, including autosomes (non-sexual chromosomes) and sex chromosomes (X and Y chromosomes). As already mentioned, chromosomes exist in pairs, and the human genetic material consists of twenty-two pairs of autosomes and one pair of sex chromosomes. In women the pair is constituted by two X chromosomes; in men, by one X and one Y chromosome. Identical DNA locations on both chromosomes of one pair are referred to as 'alleles'. In the case of a disease-causing DNA variation, we then speak of normal and abnormal alleles, which represent the two forms of the affected gene. A person carrying in his or her DNA two different alleles is said to be heterozygous for this particular allelic variation; when the two alleles are identical, the person is said to be a homozygote. The term 'allele' refers globally to the state of one genetic location compared to the state of the corresponding location on the other chromosome. The manifestation of the alternative or affected form of the gene in a given phenotype is referred to as a 'trait'.

Some diseases are expressed by a single abnormal allele while others require the presence of abnormal alleles on both chromosomes. In the first case, heterozygotes are affected by the disease and the allele (or trait) is said to be 'dominant'. In the second case, the symptoms of the disease are present only in homozygotes for the abnormal allele, which is said to be 'recessive'.

Autosomal dominant diseases result from the presence of one affected gene on one autosome. They include, among others, achondroplasia, HD, myotonic dystrophy, polyposis coli and polycystic kidney disease. As for sex-linked dominant traits, there is no representative example of a Y-linked dominant disorder. There are, however, several X-linked dominant traits, the most common being probably a disease called vitamin D-resistant rickets.

Autosomal recessive diseases are manifested only in homozygotes: both autosomes from the pair need to carry the diseased trait. Phenylketonuria and CF are two representative examples often mentioned.

X-linked recessive diseases affect female homozygotes and all male heterozygotes, because the only X chromosome of their genome carries necessarily the affected gene; haemophilia and DMD are the two best-known examples of X-linked recessive traits.

The Case of Super-males

There are no Y-linked recessive disorders for the simple reason that under normal conditions nobody bears two Y chromosomes. There are, however, rare conditions where men have been observed to carry an extra Y chromosome (and be XYY instead of XY). The media publicized this condition widely a few years back when several investigations reported that most individuals who had an XYY genotype were also violent criminals. This observation provided more evidence for defenders of the theory that excessive aggression is imprinted in Y (male) chromosomes.

Ataxia Telangiectasia and Breast Cancer

Despite the fact that it is a unifactorial monogenic disease, ataxia telangiectasia (AT) a disease affecting patients from early childhood, which is characterized by a wide range of clinical manifestations. These include degeneration of cerebellum cells (Purkinje cells), which results in a progressive ataxia or lack of movement co-ordination; extremely high sensitivity of certain types of cells to ionizing radiations such as X-rays and radiations emitted by radioactive components; chromosomal rearrangement in lymphocytes, cells whose function is to fight infections and destroy cancer cells; increased risk of cancer and cellular and humoral immunodeficiency; premature ageing; and insulin-resistant diabetes mellitus.

It shows an autosomal recessive mode of inheritance, which means that the patient must have one defective gene on each of two autosomes (non-sexual chromosomes). In other words, a patient is a homozygote for the disease. It also means that both parents are heterozygous, or are carriers of the trait; they each have one affected gene on one chromosome only.

There is currently no treatment for this devastating disease. Although we still do not know the molecular abnormality causing the disease, collaboration between no less than fourteen prestigious research centres, mostly in America but also in Canada and the Netherlands, has resulted in the approximate location of the AT gene. It is located at the beginning of the long arm of chromosome 11. As usual, the next step will be to walk along this region of chromosome 11 until the unknown gene is identified. Meanwhile, the development of a diagnostic test for AT has broader applications. Indeed, AT heterozygotes are healthy carriers of the trait. But not that 'healthy', as it turns out; their cells grown *in vitro* display a sensitivity to ionizing radiations which, although not as high as that of individuals affected by AT, is much higher than that of non-carriers. We have reason to believe that what happens in laboratory conditions happens also in the real world. It has now been demonstrated that women carriers have a higher-than-normal risk of developing breast cancer. No association with other types of cancer has been demonstrated so far, but the possibility of such associations in men as well as women should be kept in mind.

Since heterozygotes do not display the symptoms of AT, they cannot be identified unless they have conceived a child affected by the disease. A genetic test for AT will thus detect not only homozygotes but also heterozygotes, who otherwise might never know that they carry the trait in their genome. We are no longer talking about a rare disorder: the frequency of heterozygotes in the general population could be as high as 1 per cent.

Immediate measures should be undertaken in confirmed heterozygotes. Usual radiation doses used therapeutically should be decreased to the bare essential, as these could otherwise induce additional cancers among patients who would be treated for the particular form. Furthermore, heterozygotes (as, of course, homozygotes) should avoid contact with radioactive substances, whatever the dose. Meanwhile, carriers of the AT trait should be very conscientious about full medical check-ups, so that any cancer can be detected at the earliest possible opportunity.

Multifactorial Disorders

Many phenotypic characteristics and many diseases are not trans-mitted as unifactorial but as multifactorial traits. This means that their manifestations result from the interplay between the effects of several genes and the action of the environment. Height, weight, skin colour, IQ and also heart disease and some types of cancer are the result of multifactorial modes of inheritance. Multifactorial transmission does not follow Mendel's Laws: in fact, we do not understand how it works. This is why the inheritance of the few characteristics listed above remains a mystery, and why it is still impossible to predict who will suffer from, say, a heart attack or what will be the adult weight of a given child.

Even if we knew the effect of all underlying genetic factors, we would still be unable to predict the progression of these phenotypes because environmental factors add another order of difficulty. Never-theless, much progress has been made in the genetics of these traits and we have established the empiric risks of an individual being affected by a multifactorial disease. These are based on the concept of an individual's liability to a particular disease, taking into account both genetic and environmental factors. Deciphering the complexity of these diseases constitutes one of the most challenging goals of molecular genetics, forcing researchers to push the limits of feasibility of current technologies. Our understanding of multifactorial diseases will form the basis of Part Two of this book.

Development of a Genetic Test for an Inherited Disorder

Scientists use exactly the same principles for genetic studies of both monogenic and multifactorial diseases. However, monogenic disorders are simpler to conceptualize, so results are generated faster and at a lower research cost – a factor worth taking into account when grant money is hard to come by. The basic working hypothesis is that one 'abnormal' gene causes the disease. Genetic-marker technology makes it possible to locate the abnormal gene and then to identify this gene, as well as the disease-causing abnormality. Only when this has happened are scientists able to start understanding the mechanism of the disease, thereby paving the way for the elaboration of efficient treatments and even of possible cures for the genetic disease.

This is what molecular geneticists have been working on since 1978, when the first genetic test for sickle cell anaemia was reported. Looking back at it, sickle cell anaemia was an easy one, because we knew, first, what the affected protein was (beta-globin) and, second, what the protein abnormality was (glutamic acid replaced by valine at the sixth position of the beta-globin, protein). In cases like this, all molecular biologists have to do is transpose the information they have about the affected protein level to information at the corresponding DNA level. They know what DNA probe to choose: for sickle cell anaemia, it is a DNA probe derived from the gene coding for beta-globin. Several similar cases have thus been resolved and diagnostic tests developed.

Unknown Culprit: The Value of Reverse Genetics

For most genetic diseases, however, the culprit is simply not known. Clinical investigations may have resolved the mode of inheritance of a given disease, but the causative factor remains totally unknown. Yet if a disease is shown to be transmitted as an autosomal dominant trait, for example, it means that a defect of a unique gene located on an autosome is responsible for the clinical symptoms. The beauty of gene-marker technology is that we can actually develop a diagnostic test for this disease even if we have no idea what the culprit gene is. This has been the case for HD, DMD and CF.

The development of such a test involves a method called 'linkage analysis'. To be successfully applied, this requires two main components: first, a set of DNA probes detecting genetic markers all along the DNA molecule, and, second, ideally, three-generation families (called 'pedigrees' in human genetics) with several members affected by the disease under investigation. The principle is conceptually simple: it consists of finding, somewhere along the DNA molecule, one or more genetic markers which are present in the DNA of affected individuals but not in the DNA of 'healthy' family members. If they are really linked to the disease, these markers are inherited together with the disease by the successive generations of the family.

Once a genetic marker is found to be associated with the presence of the disease, molecular geneticists know that the disease-causing gene lies in the vicinity of the location of this marker. The genetic marker itself is not the cause of the disease, but it constitutes some kind of flag, signalling the presence nearby of the abnormal gene. If the marker is sufficiently close to the diseased gene, its detection constitutes a diagnostic test for the disease in question. At this point we know neither the cause of the disease nor what gene or what protein is involved, yet we have developed an accurate diagnostic test for that genetic disease. This is what a lot of people find hard to understand.

The next step is to walk, as molecular biologists say, along the DNA molecule until the abnormal gene is finally identified. The distance to cover is, at the most, a few million base pairs. If it were more than that, we would not have detected any linkage between the marker and the disease in the first place. Techniques to enable us to walk along the chromosome are based upon the detection of additional markers.

Scientists isolate DNA probes adjacent or close to the one which has detected the first linked marker. If they are going in the right direction on the DNA molecule, linkage between the new markers and the disease should get stronger and stronger. They keep on until they arrive at the location of the culprit gene. Identification of the gene involves sequencing the DNA region suspected of containing the gene; sequence data of the whole area indeed reveals the usual signal sequence found in and around all genes. Gene cloning procedures are then used to isolate the gene from a 'healthy' individual and the gene from someone affected by the disease. Comparison of the sequences of the two genes will finally identify the genetic abnormality responsible for the disease.

This process for discovering a genetic abnormality causing an inherited disease is called 'reverse genetics', because it is DNA analysis which permits us to identify the abnormal mechanisms. Since clinical investigation, protein chemistry and physiology have preceded molecular biology, we tend to assume that they should provide the information necessary to carry out DNA analysis, and not the other way around!

Reverse Genetics: Analogy with Searching for a Restaurant

To recapitulate on reverse genetics as applied to the development of diagnostic tests, the first step is to find genetic markers along the DNA molecule which, whenever they are present, are also associated with the presence of a disease. They serve as signals for the presence nearby of a disease-causing gene. A prognostic test consists of the detection of these signals. At this stage, the molecular geneticist has identified only preliminary markers and needs to walk along the DNA molecule until the culprit (the disease-causing gene abnormality) is discovered. This is done by moving from one marker to another, getting closer and closer to the diseased allele. Once the gene is finally identified, the disease-causing DNA variation can be identified too. Two practical consequences are the possibility of a more accurate test and the chance to work on effective treatment modalities.

Now, imagine that you are on a holiday in the French countryside, hiking through rolling hills and farmlands. One day you decide that your goal will be to find a good regional restaurant. Your plan is to walk to the nearest road, look for the first sign advertising such a restaurant and follow the subsequent signs (these will give you information about both the restaurant's name and distance) until you finally arrive. How can this be analogous to the search by molecular geneticists for genetic markers to identify a hereditary disease?

The restaurant is the disease-carrying gene and the road is the DNA molecule. You start at the point where a sign (the genetic marker) indicates 'Auberge du Moulin, 15 km'. The sign, however, does not tell you in which direction to go. You have to make a decision and hope it's the right one. For whatever reason, you choose to go north (chromosome walking along the DNA molecule). Maybe your decision was random; maybe it was impossible to go south because the way was closed (you do not have genomic clones – isolated pieces of the DNA molecule for walking that way); or maybe it was downhill and therefore easier (you have isolated more clones or found more markers that way).

If, having walked 8 km, you see a second sign (second genetic marker) saying 'Auberge du Moulin, 23 km', you know you have gone the wrong way, and you have to retrace your steps. If, on the other hand, the second sign reads 'Auberge du Moulin, 7 km', you are sure to be there soon. All you need to do is keep on walking. Indeed, after another 3 km a third sign (third genetic marker) informs you that the 'Auberge du Moulin' is only 4 km down the road. And so on until you finally arrive at the restaurant (the disease-causing gene) and, more to the point, you achieve your initial goal: to sit down at a particular table (a more precise part of the gene) and on a particular chair (you have identified the precise mutation which causes the disease), and eat your meal, since you have thereby developed a DNA test to predict an individual genetic susceptibility to a hereditary disease.

Unfortunately, the food is awful, the wine-waiter has no wine left (hard to believe in a French restaurant) and the waiters are rude (more likely). You are starting to think that there was not much point in coming here after all, going to all that trouble to make it (you have developed a prognostic test, but no cure, no treatment, not even the means of preventing the disease, seem to be available). However, you decide to train the chef and the staff in order to improve both the quality of the food and the attitude of the waiters, and, unbelievably, you succeed. Moreover, you discover in a hidden cellar bottles of wine aged to perfection (you have developed an effective treatment and even a cure for the disease you can predict). You can now finally relax and enjoy the sweetness of victory, overwhelmed at having accomplished your initial goal in full (a fairy-tale situation never encountered in scientific research).

Slight modifications of the story will illustrate two additional concepts relevant not only to genetic-marker technology but also to research in general: improved methodology and improved communication between scientists. Researchers constantly strive to improve the existing technologies available for them to carry out experiments; higher efficiency should lead to a greater chance of important discoveries. To get a better grasp of the significance of these improvements, let us revert to the initial road sign (first genetic marker) indicating the 'Auberge du Moulin' 15 km away. In order to reach the restaurant, you proceed as before. But instead of walking slowly, you run, or even better, you ride a bicycle or drive a car, both of which happen to be waiting for you at the first road sign. All three mean you arrive faster (you have been using improved chromosome walking techniques).

Alternatively, you can take a very fast train which stops only at the road signs (technique of chromosome jumping, where you progress along the chromosome from genetic marker to genetic marker when these are located far apart from each other). Or you can even use a helicopter which flies you directly over a 15-km stretch (chromosome hopping). In this case, if you are lucky and the restaurant has a landing permit, you can arrive right at its door (you have identified a genetic marker within the disease-carrying gene); otherwise, you attempt to land as close as possible (the genetic marker is in the vicinity of the gene) and walk or drive for the final short stretch. You have applied the same principle to reach the restaurant. However, when you improve your transportation system, you just happen to go faster and faster.

With the help of some other modifications, the story can also represent concepts of scientific collaboration and communication. Back again to the original road sign (first genetic marker), where you now arrive at the same time as another person who also wishes to enjoy a meal at the 'Auberge du Moulin'. You decide to separate and each go in a given direction (walking, jumping or hopping), and although you do not like this person, you agree to use the closed telephone system linking the road signs and communicate to each other your respective location at any given time (scientific collaboration).

In this way, if other people are interested in the results of your investigation, you can let them know about the general situation (you write a scientific article). Luck has it that you choose to move north, while your colleague goes south. Of course, after 8 km you realize that you are going in the right direction, at which point you revise your views about peer interaction and want to make sure you arrive first (and receive all the fame and glory). You are suddenly determined not to use the phone until after you have safely arrived. This procedure is called withholding information. It is a negative and counterproductive way of working which is, fortunately, encountered only rarely (but again, naïveté has always been one of my character traits!). This attitude is, in any case, inherent in human nature and not exclusive to scientists.

This little story helps us describe a complicated situation – the use of genetic markers in the identification of a hereditary disease – and makes it possible to visualize a situation which would otherwise be difficult to imagine. We have just built what is called a model. This model, like all models, is a representation of reality and not a precise account of what is really happening. But it is useful to us. We understand better an event occurring in the macroscopic world because we relate it to objects and situations we happen to be familiar with. Furthermore, slight modifications to the story or the introduction of new facts remaining within the realm of the plot provide means of representing additional concepts, including, in this case, improved genetic-engineering methodology and scientific communication. We just have to bear in mind that a model distorts reality and should not be mistaken for reality. Its function is to contain, in a few simple terms or drawings, the essence of what we know about a given subject.

Prenatal Detection of Inherited Diseases

Genetic tests are usually performed on DNA isolated from the white cells of regular blood samples. Indeed, blood samples represent convenient DNA sources and are readily available from anybody. But we should not forget that DNA is present in all tissues of the organism and is also stable throughout a person's life. A genetic test can thus be performed at any time and the result will always be the same. This includes the period before birth, starting at the time of conception, as soon as the egg is formed.

There are several ways to collect DNA from a foetus or an embryo. Drawing blood from a foetus is feasible, but it is a sensitive procedure, putting both the mother and the future child at risk. Doctors prefer by far two other sampling methods which have gained a rapid popularity. The first one is called amniocentesis. In the womb the foetus is surrounded by amniotic fluid, a protective liquid which, among other components, also contains a suspension of foetal cells. The technique of transabdominal amniocentesis makes it possible to draw a small sample of this liquid, from which enough foetal cells can be isolated to provide DNA for a prenatal test. However, to avoid any side effect, this is best done around the sixteenth week of gestation. At that time the pregnancy is already quite advanced and a termination would be associated with a deep emotional trauma for the parents, even if they know that the child would otherwise be born with a hereditary disease giving no chance of survival, or a short life marked by severe pain.

Testing is more desirable at an earlier stage and this is now achieved by chorionic villi sampling (also called chorionic biopsy), which can be performed as early as eight to ten weeks' gestation. The risks associated with both amniocentesis and chorionic villi sampling are negligible for both the mother and the child, and both methods are now becoming quite routine medical procedures.

Naturally, prenatal diagnosis is warranted only in precise cases where parents are known carriers of abnormal genes whose combination in the children can lead to devastating illnesses, or because their age increases the risk of birth defects. It is then the parents' responsibility to decide, in agreement with their physician, whether or not to terminate the pregnancy should tests prove positive.

PART TWO _____

New Times, New Diseases – a Matter of Ageing

Introduction to Part Two

THE PAST FEW DECADES HAVE SEEN A GRADUAL BUT STRIKING SHIFT in our idea of what constitutes the more pressing problems facing current clinical practice and medical research. Little more than fifty years ago medical science was preoccupied with understanding and treating the serious infectious diseases.

Though often fatal, these diseases were simple to conceptualize: a specific bacterium named Koch's bacillus was the offending agent in tuberculosis; another bacterium, the spirochete, caused syphilis. A single etiology, the infectious agent, resulted in a single malady, the infection.

The work of Louis Pasteur and of countless other scientists led to the understanding of the process of infection, from its cause to its clinical manifestations. All that was needed then was to be able to treat infections. A fantastic step was made in 1927, when the British physician and bacteriologist Alexander Fleming discovered the first antibiotic. Fleming, who was doing research on micro-organisms, noticed that colonies of bacteria (streptococci) stopped growing when they came in contact with a microscopic fungus, *Penicillium notatum*. The substance secreted by the fungus – penicillin – was then isolated, characterized and produced industrially by 1940. Penicillin's widespread use was immediate, because it brought about an extraordinarily fast cure of infections that had been lethal until then: pneumonia, pleurisy and meningitis. Its discovery also triggered countless investigations which have since led to the development of a whole spectrum of antibiotics, key molecules against infection because they act directly on the development of bacteria and fungi. Once chemicals that killed infectious agents were discovered and proved efficacious, cure was at hand. The effect on the practice of medicine was nothing short of revolutionary.

The term 'infection' now applies to all diseases caused by micro-organisms (these include viruses, chlamydiae, rickettsiae, bacteriae, spirochetes, fungi, protozoae and helminths). Infectious diseases are characterized by transmission to other people but are preventable by vaccines and hygienic measures. Due to a combination of anti-microbial chemotherapy, immunization, improved nutrition, better sanitation and better housing facilities in industrialized countries, their incidence has been continually decreasing. Most bacterial, fungal and protozoal infections are successfully treated with anti-microbial agents. The prevention of viral infections has been dras-tically improved with the use of vaccines. The field of anti-viral chemotherapy is more complicated, but it has already yielded several effective agents, including idoxuridine, acyclovir, interferon, ribavirin and zidovudine (azidothymidine, or AZT).

Today we understand the processes of infectious diseases. As a result not only have epidemics that were once the main cause of death been put under control but they are also progressively being eradicated.

After infection the next challenge for medical research has been the fight against unifactorial (or monogenic) genetic diseases. Diseases of this category are caused by single gene abnormalities. Examples include, among many others, sickle cell anaemia, phenylketonurea, HD, CF and haemophilia. The advent of molecular genetics has allowed us to comprehend monogenic diseases and to study their direct causes at the DNA level. With the method of linkage analysis, it is easy for molecular geneticists to determine the chromosomal location of the gene responsible for a particular genetic disease. They then use the technique of chromosome walking to reach and identify that gene. The detection of a diseased gene with genetic markers, or any other method, constitutes a diagnostic test for that disease. Development of diagnostic tests is the stage that medical researchers have reached. The major task for the immediate future is, using our newly acquired knowledge of molecular causes, to elaborate appropriate therapies. However, it still seems at this point that conventional methods of drug development are more successful than the techniques of molecular biology.

In recent years both the diseases that represent major public health worries and our understanding of the processes that might lead to their treatment or prevention stand in stark contrast to such a simple one agent—one disease—one cure model. As the early, acute mortality of infectious diseases has for the most part been brought under control in industrialized countries, and as the puzzle of monogenic disorders is quickly being solved, the practice of medicine and medical research have turned to a whole range of disorders that can be best described as chronic and degenerative in nature. Cardiovascular disease (disease of the heart and of the vessels), including atherosclerosis, hypertension and diabetes, some forms of cancer, osteoporosis, asthma, dementia of the Alzheimer's type and schizophrenia are all examples of diseases that are insidious in onset, often affect the middle-aged and elderly and cause a gradual erosion in an individual's quality of life, as well as consuming millions of pounds in health care money each year. These diseases, which are sometimes referred to as 'modern diseases', seem to be the result of ageing. We fear them because we know that they can strike randomly, because we are always unprepared to confront their appearance and also because we feel powerless in the face of their consequences, which are always devastating.

Considered one by one, these chronic, degenerative types of diseases are often difficult to conceptualize. There is no single, clearly defined etiological agent for most of them, let alone understanding of an optimal treatment modality. For certain general categories, there is not even a single, clearly defined disease entity.

In this respect cancer, for example, is not a unique disease. There are many types of cancer, and each type is due to an abnormality in a particular mechanism, even if the ultimate consequence is an anarchic cell proliferation. Heart disease is not a disease: it is a complicated, heterogeneous mixture of unrelated disorders which show themselves by a plethora of clinical manifestations. Schizophrenia is not a mental disease; what is referred to by this name is a clinical entity with a more or less defined group of symptoms which are the result of several different causes.

In fact, these two fundamental characteristics – complex origins and complex manifestations – are the hallmarks of the majority of such chronic disease processes – hence the term 'multifactorial' widely used to define them. Expression of a multifactorial disease results from the combination of two types of factors – genetic and environmental – but we should not let ourselves be fooled. 'Multifactorial' is a vague term which translates perfectly our weak understanding of these disease processes. To say that a disease is multifactorial is a way to hide our ignorance. We know very little indeed about these diseases, yet they cause much concern for the individual and cost society an enormous amount of money.

So many studies have demonstrated the presence of inherited components in modern diseases that nobody challenges this observation any more. Yet the mode of transmission for many of them remains a mystery. They do not follow the classic Mendelian laws of inheritance. The problem is that we are not talking about one specific gene abnormality as a cause. We are after genetic susceptibilities. Several genetic factors predispose a person to a particular disease; conditions of the environment do the rest. Researchers run into major difficulties trying to isolate either one or other of these factors. In fact, the contributing effect of one given gene in the onset of a multifactorial disease is weak, because it is diluted among the effects of the other factors – both hereditary and environmental. The smaller the effect, the larger the sample size: the detection of this effect requires the study of a very large number of patients affected by this particular disease – which is often the limiting resource of these research investigations.

This is why the most we can generally say is that heart disease or cancer 'run in families'. Clearly, some families appear particularly predisposed to lipid disorders, others to cancer, others to hypertension, others still to mental diseases. There are so many afflictions that any family in the world is predisposed to something labelled as deleterious. Some investigators have advanced the theory that each person carries traits for at least five or six major disorders, but this estimate could be challenged. I personally think that it is very conservative. Whatever, the message is that no one escapes the lottery of life: we all draw adverse traits. Let us not forget, though, that we all win life itself.

An understanding of the progression patterns of modern diseases – to which molecular biology is greatly contributing – helps the whole field of medicine to design strategies for prevention. Progress towards that end has been simply amazing and in Part Two we will be looking at what we have learned about heart disease, hypertension, obesity, cancer, allergy and some mental disorders.

7

Heart Disease Revisited

MR MEYER WAS QUITE A CHARACTER IN THE VILLAGE WHERE I USED TO spend my summer holidays as a child. He had been the mayor for over twenty years, but what singled him out was his way of life. He drank brandy with his morning coffee, many glasses of wine at every meal, beer in between and never skipped an opportunity to add an extra apéritif. I remember that he was always smoking a cigar – his favourite ones came from Switzerland. He was also particularly fond of rich, heavy, country food. His motto could have been 'enjoy life while you can' . . . and he died at the age of ninety, after falling from a tree in which he was picking cherries. We all have similar stories of people who seem to be immune to the damaging consequences of life's excesses.

On the other hand, there are many stories which are quite the opposite, and are terribly unfair. Take my friend Ben. Ben always made a point of sticking to a regular schedule and to a healthy diet. He was fervently anti-smoking and anti-alcohol, and he believed strongly in the virtues of physical exercise. He died from a heart attack at the age of thirty-nine while jogging in a park.

Disease, a Natural Form of Discrimination

We are not equal in the face of disease, and the word that comes naturally to mind when thinking about its way of striking randomly is 'unfair'. Heart disease, for example, appears to be quite unpredictable. Our anecdotal observations are backed up by epidemiologists' statistics.

The French are fond of good food, rich in cream and fat; they do not particularly enjoy strenuous physical exercise (compared to California, very few people are seen jogging in the streets of France); and they smoke. Yet they have one of the lowest incidences of death from heart disease (325 men out of 100,000) among industrialized countries, bettered only by Japan (310/100,000). In America, where the average serum cholesterol level in the population is similar to what it is in France, the mortality rate from heart disease reaches 507 per 100,000. It is interesting to note that this rate is 774/100,000 in Poland and 820/100,000 in Hungary.

Atherosclerosis, or Hardening of the Arteries

Many factors are implicated in the onset of heart disease and we are barely beginning to understand their effect in different individuals and in different populations of individuals.

Heart disease is the major underlying disorder of cardiovascular disease, a clinical entity encompassing all disorders of the heart and blood vessels. Cardiovascular disease is at present the leading cause of mortality in industrialized countries: ultimately, almost one person out of two dies from its complications. My aim in this chapter is to focus on atherosclerotic heart disease, or heart disease caused by the effects of atherosclerosis.

Atherosclerosis is due to a progressive deposition of cholesterol in the cell walls of arteries. It affects mostly medium- and large-sized arteries, and this is why it is so damaging. The function of arterial blood is to bring oxygen and metabolites (food) to the various tissues of the organism (while venous blood removes carbon dioxide and cellular-degradation products). Arteries and other blood vessels can be compared to plastic, pliable tubes and atheromatous lesions to waste deposits accumulating within the inner wall, thereby hardening and plugging the tubing. At some sites they either end up completely clogged or too narrow to permit adequate flow; blood clots (thrombi) remain stuck and obstruct the passage. The obstruction cuts off the blood supply to the downstream tissues. One immediate, damaging consequence is the destruction (necrosis) of the tissues due to lack of oxygen (an infarct). A stroke consists of the obstruction of a blood vessel causing the destruction of a brain area. The myocardium, or heart muscle, can be similarly damaged. Obstruction of one or more coronary arteries, which irrigate and feed the myocardium, results in a myocardial infarction, or heart attack.

This slow, insidious and somehow irreversible cholesterol deposition begins as early as childhood, but its clinical manifestations – including heart disease, cerebrovascular accidents and peripheral vascular disease – typically do not appear before middle age. In other words, the disease process begins long before its clinical symptoms.

Several types of cells participate in the formation of atheromatous plaques (or lesions). These include platelets, endothelial cells, tissue macrophages and smooth muscle cells. Their accumulation in the inner part of the blood vessels is followed by coating with fibrous layers and further hardening with calcium deposits. For this reason, many researchers consider atherosclerosis to be a proliferative (rather than degenerative) process.

Heart disease has always been a major subject of preoccupation – probably more than any other disease. There are several reasons, economic incentives not the least of them. In America alone, the yearly cost of treatment of heart disease complications has been estimated at over $80 billion! Heart disease is so prevalent that it casts a shadow over everyone, either personally or because a member of the family or a friend has been affected. Its effects are always devastating, leaving behind either death or severe and debilitating consequences.

Besides, the heart itself is fascinating. First of all, it is a very hard worker. Beating non-stop throughout life at an average of 100,000 beats every day, it pumps about 10,000 litres of blood in the process through a capillary network which is 60,000 miles long. But it represents more than a mere pumping muscle; it symbolizes life, courage, love, happiness and suffering. The symbolic importance of the heart is reflected in the many expressions we use: 'to put one's heart into it', 'broken heart', 'hearty', 'my heart isn't in it', 'he lost his heart', etc.

The Many Risk Factors in Heart Disease

Many factors are reported to be associated with the development of atherosclerotic heart disease. Age and sex, smoking, positive family history, elevated blood lipid levels (hyperlipidaemiae), hypertension, diabetes, obesity, lack of physical exercise, ethnic origin, stress, personality factors, blood-clotting factors, oral contraceptives and genetic factors have all been found to confer an overall increased risk for heart disease in the general population. Disease factors are statistical concepts determined from large-scale investigations, and their effects on an individual are quite variable. A person affected by hypertension or by hyperlipidaemia is more at risk of developing heart disease than the norm that has been determined by studying populations. This does not mean that the person will necessarily develop heart disease, just that the odds are higher. Combinations of risk factors increase greatly these odds. For example, the odds conferred by the presence of all the above-mentioned factors would be so high as to make a heart attack unavoidable. Fortunately, it is rare to observe more than a few of them in any given individual.

Medical texts always list disease factors independently, as I have just done. Yet we know that they are somewhat interrelated, are not really independent, even if we can explain only a few of the relationships. For example, genetic factors should not be listed separately, because they are implicated at the same time in the mechanisms of hypertension, diabetes, hyperlipidaemia and obesity.

With respect to atherosclerosis, health is controlled by a delicate balance: there should be enough cholesterol and other fats to satisfy the organism's requirement, but not too much; that way the excess can be cleared out of the body without leaving any damaging trace. The development of atherosclerosis results from an inability on the body's part to handle properly varying loads of cholesterol. The cause of this inability lies in the effect of genetic factors implicated in molecular pathways of lipid transport, metabolism (biochemical reactions), storage and clearance of blood-clotting and many other known or unknown mechanisms.

Heart disease is more prevalent among men. Women are protected until menopause through the action of hormonal mechanisms that we still do not understand. Afterwards, their risk increases but never reaches that of men, and on average a ten-year-gap always remains between the respective risks of the two genders. Stress and personality factors are directly implicated in the development of atherosclerotic heart disease. More aggressive type-A personalities are more prone to myocardial infarction, but since these individuals are more ready to fight for their lives, their overall mortality rate from heart disease may not be significantly higher as they seem to recuperate better.

The effect of psychological factors can be important: panic attacks can mimic the symptoms of a heart attack. Data from a well-controlled study showed that maybe up to 16 per cent of people brought to an emergency room with chest pains and pounding hearts were suffering from panic attacks. Although there are many exceptions, a panic attack victim is typically a woman in her twenties or thirties, while a typical heart attack patient is a middle-aged man. Panic attack, described as a separate disease entity since the 1880s, is one of the two major forms of what psychiatrists call anxiety neurosis (the other form is chronic anxiety and includes phobias and hypochondriasis). The patient suffering from anxiety is in a state of fear and feels tense. Sweating, tremor and elevated heart rate constitute the common symptomatic manifestations. There is a genetic predisposition to anxiety, which is then triggered by a variety of painful events: bereavement, divorce, combat duty, hostile environment, loss of a career. Panic attacks can usually be prevented with anti-depressants and other medications. The diagnosis of anxiety neurosis is invariably made difficult by the fact that the patient tends to fail to mention the distressing emotional component and focus only on peripheral (somatic) symptoms. The sole value of the very expensive cardiac tests that are prescribed is to rule out heart disease. Anxiety remains often undiagnosed and therefore untreated.

Should We Really Lower Our Cholesterol Levels?

Hyperlipidaemia, and in particular elevated blood-cholesterol levels, is widely considered to be the most important risk factor in athero-sclerotic heart disease. After all, atheromatous lesions are mostly made up of cholesterol. No wonder, then, that there has been so much talk, over the past few years, about cholesterol. Its name has been mentioned so many times that we are getting tired of it. However, we are now beginning to question the validity of the numerous anti-cholesterol campaigns that have been so successfully launched. We may have been too quick in oversimplifying the problem of mortality due to atherosclerosis and blaming cholesterol for every single problem. The complication has arisen because we tend to take individual risk factors out of their proper contexts and forget complex interactions. Most studies have concentrated solely on the association between cholesterol and heart disease, without consideration of other factors.

Cholesterol, a natural constituent of the organism, is of major biological importance. It is a molecule of fat (a lipid), produced for the most part by the liver itself. The remainder is provided by ingested food. In general, the amount of cholesterol which can be synthesized by our liver is about ten times greater than the amount ingested in a normal Western diet. This explains why low-cholesterol diets have little effect on the blood levels of certain people.

Found in all cells of the body, cholesterol is an indispensable struc-tural component of cellular membranes, in which it also regulates the passage and exchange of chemicals with other cells. It is the precursor of steroid hormones, vitamin D and bile salts, without which digestion and absorption of dietary fats would be impossible. Present essentially in animal fat, it is absent in vegetables.

However, cholesterol is also associated with several adverse effects, and nobody can play these down. As mentioned earlier, atheromatous lesions are constituted for the most part of cholesterol deposits. Animals fed on cholesterol-rich diets develop arterial lesions similar to human atheromas. The overall population incidence of mortality caused by myocardial infarction raises with increasing levels of blood cholesterol. Conversely, reduction of serum cholesterol levels by diet or by drug therapy contributes to a lowering of the frequency of coronary disease.

The definition of ideal blood-cholesterol levels has been and continues to be much debated. These levels should be kept within a certain range, spanning average values observed among people who seem healthy with respect to heart disease. We have to keep in mind, however, that the concentration of cholesterol in the blood increases regularly with age. In any case, medical organizations in industrialized countries generally agree on critical upper levels: 160 to 180 mg/dl in younger individuals; 200 mg/dl in older people. When the observed cholesterol levels are above these cut-off values, we speak of hypercholesterolemia, a diagnosis which generally sets off alarm bells in the population. In fact, the predictive value of higher cholesterol levels seems to be effective until the age of sixty. Afterwards, the risk of myocardial infarction becomes more and more independent of blood cholesterol, and one out of two heart attacks strikes individuals with normal values.

The trend today is systematically to lower the circulating cholesterol levels. The question is, by how much? In the light of the results of surveys showing a link between cholesterol-level decrease and decreased cardiovascular disease, we might think that the more, the better, but this is not so. A report in the *Lancet* in April 1989 shows that women over sixty have a five times greater mortality rate when their serum cholesterol falls down to 150 mg/dl. In this respect, it is preferable to have a cholesterol level of 350 mg/dl. The cause of higher mortality associated with low cholesterol is not clear. It was not due, as might have been thought, to malnutrition; the subjects were found to have balanced diets. Cancer has been put forward as the reason, but this has been challenged lately. Another study involving male subjects has confirmed that lowering high cholesterol levels is associated with decreased mortality from heart disease. However, these men die from other, as yet undetermined, causes, so the overall mortality is unchanged!

The conclusion of several large-scale investigations is that the overall mortality rate from all causes is at its lowest when the serum cholesterol level is 270 mg/dl – which is considered to be indicative of a moderately high hypercholesterolemia!

We do not yet fully understand all the processes leading to heart disease. A high level of serum cholesterol constitutes one of the many risk factors. However, because it is not the only one, its predictive value is limited. Dietary cholesterol does not necessarily have much to do with circulating levels or incidence of myocardial infarction. Although in Finland large amounts of saturated fats in the diet are accompanied by one of the highest rates of cardiovascular disease in the world, in Crete and Tibet the low incidence of cardiovascular disease can be explained by low-cholesterol diets. The Masai, however, who drink up to five litres of whole milk every day, have low serum levels of cholesterol and a very low rate of myocardial infarction.

In America 'prudent' diets, non-smoking campaigns and controlled blood pressure have contributed to a steadily declining death rate from myocardial infarction – down by 40 per cent – over the past twenty years. Meanwhile, the population's mean cholesterol level has been reduced by 2.75 per cent. If we refer to our current risk tables, this reduction should be associated with a 5.5 per cent decreased rate of heart disease, not 40 per cent.

For a long time cholesterol has been considered as a predictor for heart disease, but we know now that the equation is not that simple. Indeed, cholesterol is not the only circulating lipid derived from digestion and from synthesis by the organism. There are also phospholipids and triglycerides, whose roles in the body are fundamental. Phospholipids represent basic components of cell membranes. Triglycerides, found in both animals and plants, are the major dietary source of lipids. Synthesized and stored by the organism, they make up most of our body fat. Although it is commonly admitted that elevated blood triglyceride levels are indicative of risk for cardiovascular disease, their predictive value is much weaker than that of cholesterol and their association with heart disease is still unclear.

Good and Bad Cholesterols

Then there is the question of 'good' and 'bad' cholesterol – confusing terminology for many! A cholesterol molecule is a cholesterol molecule; it is neither good nor bad, nor does it undergo magic transformations. What is referred to here is the existence of lipoproteins. All lipids are insoluble in water or aqueous solutions, such as blood, in which they are transported. This property greatly hampers their transport. Consequently, lipids are transported in the blood in the form of particles called lipoproteins, which are aggregates of proteins and lipids. Specific proteins, the apolipoproteins, bind to the lipids and coat them; the protein part remaining in contact with the blood solution is soluble. As a consequence, the lipoprotein particle, made up of an insoluble lipid core surrounded by a soluble protein coat, can remain dissolved in all body fluids.

Among the several types of existing lipoproteins, two have attracted particular attention: high-density lipoproteins (HDL), and low-density lipoproteins (LDL). The terminology of lipoproteins is derived from the laboratory technique used for their respective separations: ultracentrifugation. Ultracentrifugation separates molecules according to their relative density; dense HDL particles move further in the separating solution than LDL particles, hence their respective names.

The function of LDL is to carry cholesterol to the cells that need it. After binding to specific receptors on the cell surface called LDL receptors, LDL particles are internalized and, inside the cell, are degraded, producing cholesterol. There is probably another type of receptor to help out if, for some reason, LDL concentrations become too high. As in the case of total cholesterol, serum levels of LDL are quite variable. High LDL levels are associated with increased incidence of atherosclerotic heart disease. This is why LDL is called 'bad cholesterol'. Indeed, excessive production of LDL or defects in its clearance mechanisms result in the deposition of its cholesterol in arteries, thereby aggravating atheromatous lesions.

The role of HDL is to ensure a retrograde transport of cholesterol from the tissues of the organism to the liver, where it is degraded. High HDL levels mean that cholesterol is efficiently cleared out of the body and have been shown to reduce the risk of heart disease. HDL is thus the 'good cholesterol'.

Low HDL and high LDL serum concentrations, now widely accepted as predictive variables for heart disease, are determined routinely in many clinical laboratories. Advances in the methodologies of clinical chemistry have added another level of refinement. HDL particles themselves can be further separated into at least three subfractions, named HDL-1, HDL-2 and HDL-3. A few exploratory studies have demonstrated that only HDL-2 is associated with a protective effect against heart disease. Before that observation was known, several investigators had shown that physical exercise contributed to increased HDL concentrations in the blood; this gives some clue about the benefits of exercise. Much media coverage was then given to an article which stated that alcohol intake also raised HDL levels. On the basis of these two observations, many observers advocated drinking alcohol to replace physical exercise as a protective measure against the progression of heart disease! Shortly after, however, it became clear that exercise is associated, as expected, with increased HDL-2, while alcohol contributes to a rise in HDL-3.

Scientists have already gone one step beyond measuring HDL and

LDL levels, and now prefer to determine directly the amount of protein constituting lipoprotein particles. The major protein component of LDL is apolipoprotein B, and that of HDL is apolipoprotein AI. Their association with atherosclerotic heart disease follows what had been determined with HDL and LDL: high apolipoprotein AI levels and low apolipoprotein B levels are desirable to prevent heart disease, and vice versa. Experts in the field of lipid disorders commonly admit that combinations of HDL and LDL values, or of apolipoprotein AI and apolipoprotein B, are better predictors than cholesterol alone.

Elaborate Choreography of All Lipoproteins

HDL and LDL are but two of the circulating lipoproteins, ensuring transport, metabolism and delivery of the various lipids. These functions involve other lipoproteins as well, including very low-density lipoprotein (VLDL), intermediate density lipoprotein (IDL) and chylomicrons. All these separate lipoproteins are related to each other. They undergo successive reactions in which lipids are removed, added and chemically modified by the action of enzymes, and where apolipoproteins are exchanged.

Chylomicrons are formed in the intestinal epithelial cells from apolipoproteins and food-derived cholesterol, triglycerides and phospholipids. After entering the circulation, they gradually lose their triglycerides, which are taken up by the various tissues of the body. Some of the chylomicron remnants go to the liver to be degraded and the remaining parts of the pool exchange cholesterol and apolipoproteins with HDL particles produced by the liver.

VLDL particles, rich in triglycerides, are synthesized by the liver. In the blood circulation they lose their triglycerides and are transformed progressively into smaller particles and finally into LDL particles. The lipoprotein family thus constitutes a complicated, interrelated system which handles the circulation of lipids around the human body.

The classification of primary lipid disorders elaborated by Donald Fredrickson is based on clinical presentation and the observed lipid abnormalities of the patient. Indeed, any lipoprotein, cholesterol or triglyceride level can be affected, and all combinations of abnormalities have been reported to date. For example, common hypercholesterolemia is characterized by increased cholesterol and LDL levels. Another disease entity called familial combined hyperlipidaemia is defined by elevated LDL, VLDL, cholesterol and triglyceride levels, with concomitant lowered HDL levels.

The Latest Fashion: Lipoprotein A

A more recently discovered blood-cholesterol-carrying particle has been added to the list of variables predicting the progression of heart disease: lipoprotein a, or lp(a), whose constituent protein is apolipoprotein A. Lp(a), whose elevated serum levels are associated with increased incidence of coronary heart disease, constitutes an independent risk factor. It seems that its production is genetically programmed, irrespective of the cholesterol present in the bloodstream. Compared to LDL, lp(a) concentrations are not affected by diet or cholesterol-lowering agents. In fact, its value as an independent predictor for heart disease is so striking that some laboratories have already started to introduce measurements of lp(a) serum levels in their tests.

Its additional research value is that, besides being a predictor of heart disease, lp(a) represents a direct link between atherosclerosis and blood-clotting mechanisms. Indeed, part of its protein structure resembles that of another protein, plasminogen. Plasminogen is involved in a pathway whose function is to dissolve blood clots formed in the vessels. The structural similarity of both proteins suggests that lp(a) probably competes with plasminogen in the binding to its natural ligand and thus inhibits the normal process targeted towards dissolving blood clots.

Lp(a) is a very good example of a molecule involved at the same time in the two general mechanisms leading to a heart attack – development of atherosclerosis and formation of blood clots. Most heart attacks are caused by blood clots forming directly at the sites of atheromatous lesions in the coronary arteries. The incidence of heart attacks is accompanied by an age-related increase in the tendency of the blood to produce clots. Although we do not quite understand this process, we have started to identify the many reactions involved. The key protein responsible for the final step of clot formation is an enzyme called thrombin. The biochemical pathway of thrombin synthesis is under the control of several separate systems that inhibit its production or block its action. Among the many proteins playing a role in the regulation of thrombin activity, the most studied have been antithrombin, heparin, thrombomodulin and protein C.

Treatments of Lipid Disorders

Although some lipid disorders can be controlled by diet, more serious conditions require drug treatment. Fortunately, a battery of medications is available and allows fairly good management of all types of lipid disorders. Physicians have at their disposal a variety of drugs adapted to all the different conditions that they encounter. Cholestyramine and cholestipol, probucol, derivatives of fibric acid such as gemfibrozil, and nicotinic acid are among the most widely used.

There has been much talk lately about the value of omega-3 unsaturated fatty acids, such as are found in fish oils. The media have seized the results from preliminary data to promote fish oil to the ranks of miracle, natural drugs to fight the progression of atherosclerosis. Omega-3 fatty acids undoubtedly have some beneficial effects, but at this point more data is needed to assess what these really are. Their main application concerns hypertriglyceridemia, but they are not advised for the treatment of hypercholesterolemia. They are very unsaturated, and that means that their degradation results in the production of toxic oxidation products. They should be used under medical supervision, and always in conjunction with antioxidants.

The most suitable drugs for the treatment of hypercholesterolemia seem to be inhibitors of hydroxy-methyl-glutaryl coenzyme A reductase (or HMG CoA Reductase). This enzyme is responsible for the synthesis of cholesterol by the liver; inhibition of its activity impairs cholesterol synthesis. They include mevilonin, synvinolin and SQ 31,000. Initial results of human clinical trials have been very promising: both circulating cholesterol and LDL levels are drastically reduced. A word of caution, however, applies to one of their side effects (all medications, whether for treating atherosclerosis or any other affliction, have potential side effects). Since they are teratogenic (will damage a foetus), they must not be given to women of childbearing age; they can be used only by men and post-menopausal women.

The Need for Predicting an Individual's Susceptibility to Heart Disease

Researchers have drawn up quite an extensive list of factors contributing directly or indirectly to the onset of atherosclerotic heart disease. The importance of early detection of an individual's predisposition to heart disease is underscored by the fact that effective, albeit inconvenient, long-term preventive intervention is available to reduce some of the morbidity and mortality of atherosclerosis.

Current predictive variables used to determine which individuals are at risk of developing clinically significant atherosclerosis include all disease factors mentioned earlier: family history of the disease, the presence of certain environmental factors (smoking history, adverse life style, psychological stressors), obesity, diabetes, hypertension, as well as serum lipid and lipoprotein levels. All of these are signs (or markers) that may indicate a propensity to atheromatous lesions.

Cholesterol and triglyceride levels, for example, can be measured with great accuracy, although substantial variation can occur between different clinical laboratories. In any case, they do not correlate very highly with either true susceptibility to atherosclerosis or actual presence of the disease state. They only indicate trends, statistical risks gathered from large-scale population studies. All we can say is that they increase the odds of someone suffering one day from a heart attack, but there is no certainty that it will happen. In fact, in extreme cases there are people with very high cholesterol levels who do not develop atherosclerosis and others with low levels who do.

The difficulty in predicting the onset of atherosclerosis stems from the multifactorial, polygenic nature of the disease. As expected, combinations of predictive variables increase the power of prediction. Many specialized lipid-disorder laboratories have come up with their own cocktail of risk factors, integrated in what statisticians call a multilogistic function. The predictive value increases rapidly with the first few factors; after five to ten of these factors, however, it reaches a plateau since most of them are not really independent but somehow related to each other. Multilogistic functions are certainly better predictors than individual disease factors, but they are still not good enough for accurate, definitive determination of susceptibility to atherosclerosis.

The most reliable diagnostic method to detect the presence of atherosclerosis in coronary arteries is a radiologic process called coronary angiography. It consists of injecting a radioactive tracer directly in the heart vessels, which can then be seen radiographically in order to determine the sites and thickness of atheromatous lesions. There are two major drawbacks in the use of coronary angiography. First, it is a highly invasive procedure, necessitating surgical intervention, which puts the patient at risk. And second, it offers too little too late, for by the time atheromatous lesions are radiographically detectable, the most appropriate time for vigorous preventive intervention has passed. Its main benefit, however, is to provide an overall picture of the state of coronary arteries, invaluable information to cardiovascular surgeons who need to decide which parts of the arteries they need to by-pass in the coronary surgery. In no way, though, can coronary angiography be employed on a routine screening basis; nor can it be applied to specific groups selected, for example, on the basis of family history.

Strategies for Prevention

At whom should prevention programmes be targeted? There are two general strategies to reduce the incidence of coronary heart disease, one aimed at the population as a whole, the other at individuals.

General population strategy aims at decreasing the overall risk of coronary heart disease in the population by changing society's nutritional habits. Several specific aims have been highlighted by the industrialized countries: weight control; decreasing cholesterol levels by reduction of dietary cholesterol down to 300 mg per day or less; reduction of dietary saturated fatty acids and replacement by mono- and polyunsaturated fatty acids; and increasing the amount of fibre in the diet.

Individual, or high-risk, strategy aims at specifically targeting the implementation of rigorous diets and drug therapies to individuals who, because of their genetic susceptibility, have a higher risk of developing atherosclerotic heart disease.

The two strategies are not mutually exclusive but are complementary. The irony is, however, that high-risk patients do not reap the benefits of the measures applied to the general population. The intervention they need can be undertaken only when the extent of their risk has been determined. Society's current view favours preventive measures targeted to the whole population. However, it would make more sense to concentrate on the high-risk group, which represents only 20 per cent of the population. How about the remaining 80 per cent? Should they adapt to nutritional and life-style changes initially designed for the benefit of a mere 20 per cent, who end up not benefiting from the changes anyway? This is a major objection that has recently surfaced. Moreover, cholesterol reduction in hypercholesterolemic individuals might be of utmost importance, but its advantage to healthy individuals has not been proved. Not to mention that lowering serum cholesterol to below 160 mg/dl increases the overall mortality rate, even if we do not know the cause and effect relationship of this phenomenon.

The message is twofold. First, we should modify our dietary habits, though there is no need to overdo it. Actually, concern about cholesterol and other health-related factors exists all over the industrialized world but is expressed in different ways. For example, I have noticed that northern Californians turn it into a religion;

southern Californians adopt appropriate measures to look good; and the French think about it, but not when they are eating out. Second, it is clear that we need to develop more sensitive and more precise tests to identify high-risk individuals. This is what molecular geneticists intend to achieve.

Hereditary Factors in Heart Disease

Epidemiological studies have repeatedly provided indirect evidence for the major role played by heredity in the process of atherosclerosis. Although it is extremely difficult to quantify these observations, heredity seems to be more significant than environmental factors. Yet it is interesting to notice the reluctance of the public to accept the role of genetic factors in a disease such as atherosclerosis.

I recently met a friend whom I had not seen since he was in medical school. He is now a practising cardiologist in a small town. What did we almost immediately talk about? Recent advances in the field of lipid disorders. When I mentioned the part played by heredity, he answered: 'Yes, but it applies only to a very specific, small group of patients who have high blood levels of cholesterol.' He meant familial hypercholesterolemia.

He seemed puzzled at first when I told him that genetic components were involved in all forms of atherosclerosis to a certain extent. Then he said, 'Oh, this is nothing new, really. The role of genetic factors has been known for a long time.'

It took him a while to realize his two statements were contradictory. The fragmented state of knowledge on the subject displayed by my friend is quite representative. It certainly does not mean that he is not a good cardiologist – his reputation proves otherwise – just that the connection between genetics and coronary heart disease is a subject still in its infancy.

We should not fall into the trap at the other extreme and pretend that everything is a question of genetics. It is not. However, the time has come to understand the genetic predispositions of individuals to heart disease.

As we now know, atherosclerosis is characterized by a whole spectrum of defects resulting from various combinations of factors, genetic and environmental. The genetic end would be represented by unifactorial, monogenic diseases, transmitted according to the classic Mendelian laws of heredity. There are several suspected cases where a single gene defect causes atherosclerosis with concomitant heart disease. Among the three or four that have already been identified, familial hypercholesterolemia (FH) constitutes the best-described example. FH is inherited as an autosomal dominant disorder and about one person in 500 carries the trait. It is due to abnormalities in the LDL receptor molecules, which do not recognize their natural ligand, LDL. Circulating LDL and cholesterol levels are very high because LDL particles are no longer taken up by the cells. Even if a low-cholesterol diet is followed, the liver produces too much cholesterol and the organism cannot handle it. Instead it is deposited in the arteries and tendons, where it is visible as xanthomas. FH heterozygotes (carrying one affected chromosome) typically suffer a heart attack in their thirties; FH homozygotes (who have both chromosomes affected) can die of myocardial infarction before the age of five.

The research teams of Mike Brown and Joe Goldstein of the University of Texas, Dallas, elucidated the mechanism of FH, for which they were awarded the Nobel Prize for Physiology and Medicine in 1985. They isolated the LDL receptor gene and determined its location on chromosome 19. What came out of their studies was that even in the case of a 'one gene–one disease' disorder causing atherosclerosis, such as FH, the problem was not that simple. In all FH families that they initially studied, the disease was indeed caused by LDL receptor-gene abnormalities, but each family carried its own particular defect. There were as many LDL receptor-gene abnormalities as affected families. Under these conditions, it is impossible to develop a genetic test for FH.

Besides, another finding complicates the matter at hand, although this one is to the advantage of some patients. It would appear that about a quarter of FH subjects, even though they have very high cholesterol levels, in the range of 500–1,000 mg/dl, show 'clean' arteries (devoid of atheromatous lesions) upon coronary angiography. This suggests the existence of protective mechanisms preventing cholesterol deposition in arteries. These mechanisms are so efficient that they overcome the effects of FH. Finding a way to boost them would lead to the development of a major therapeutic and preventive method.

An affliction such as FH represents a type of atherosclerosis caused exclusively by genetic factors. The other end of the spectrum is represented by forms of atherosclerosis due to environmental factors. Obviously, even if a person starts with a body fit for fighting atherosclerosis, excesses will wipe out genetic advantages. An overly fat-rich diet, high alcohol consumption and smoking can destroy any organism – if not from heart disease, then from cancer or cirrhosis.

Genetic Testing to Determine a Person's Predisposition to Heart Disease

The development of atherosclerotic heart disease can result from any combination of genetic and environmental factors. The presence of hereditary components in atherosclerosis makes this disease amenable to the techniques of molecular genetics, but its intricate and complex underlying mechanisms make it a puzzle that is extremely difficult to solve. However, research teams worldwide have set their minds to the formidable task of deciphering it, and data generated over the past nine years prove that they are on the right track.

One of the immediate goals of molecular geneticists is to develop prognostic tests to determine an individual's genetic susceptibility to atherosclerotic heart disease. There is no question of replacing current predictive variables such as serum cholesterol and lipoprotein levels. Their aim is simply to add genetic testing to the panoply of existing predictive methods in order to improve the accuracy of the prediction.

The availability of such genetic tests will have another fundamental consequence of more direct importance to everyone. Knowing your predisposition to atherosclerosis could allow you to determine how far you can go and what kind of excesses you can tolerate without having to incur damaging side effects.

The principle behind the development of these genetic tests is similar to the one applied to monogenic disorders, although the polygenic nature of atherosclerosis introduces an additional order of complexity. It consists of finding a battery of genetic markers associated with clinical manifestations of atherosclerotic heart disease. The first experimental step involves the identification of RFLPs; the second step involves determining which of these RFLPs correlate with the clinical symptoms of the disease.

Gene-Marker Technology Applied to Heart Disease

Genetic markers can be used in two different research strategies: linkage analysis and association studies. As mentioned already, the basis for linkage analysis is to determine the amount of linkage between an RFLP and a given gene within an extended family. Linkage indicates the presence of a gene physically located in the vicinity of a marker under study. The gene may or may not be transmitted with the marker; it will not be if they are so far apart that genetic recombination occurs between the two. The recombination rate influences the accuracy of the information provided by linkage analysis. Linkage analysis is particularly appropriate when the disease under study is known or felt to be monogenic in nature – which in most instances is not the case in atherosclerosis. Moreover, current statistical programmes handle poorly the information about hereditary transmission of several genes at the same time. Families under study are necessarily affected by one particular form of atherosclerosis (or at the most by a small number of them). By restricting the investigations to isolated families, the risk of missing many other disease types is great. This is why the first exploration of potential genes involved in the processes of atherosclerosis is best undertaken with the other strategy: association studies.

Association studies delineate the amount of association between a gene marker and a clinical phenotype in a given population. They are based on a concept of statistical rather than physical proximity. This involves the determination of the presence of a marker at higher or lower frequencies in patient DNAs when compared to the DNAs from disease-free controls derived from the same population. Association studies are more appropriately applied to multifactorial, polygenic disorders for which the mode of transmission is unknown. The total number of patients and controls can be as large as is desired and is limited only by the number of DNA samples that a research team can handle (which can be quite high; in my laboratory six technicians could carry out exploratory studies on 2,000 DNA samples in three months).

Patients Are Difficult to Differentiate from Healthy Individuals

As strange as it may appear, the overriding difficulty in carrying out gene-marker technology applied to multifactorial disorders stems from the difficulty of distinguishing between patients and controls. Theoretically, the design of the experiment calls for a group of patients affected by the disease under investigation who can be compared to a group of age- and sex-matched controls who are free of the disease. It seems straightforward but it is not. Atherosclerosis is not a yes or no (present or absent) disease.

One or more coronary arteries can be affected by atheromatous lesions of varying severity at a few or many different sites. Its multifactorial nature makes atherosclerosis a continuous rather than dichotomous variable. The application of standard statistical procedures requires that scientists define a cut-off value above which the variable confers a status of 'patient' to a subject and under which the subject is considered a 'control'. The problem is that definition criteria vary between laboratories to the point where a patient in one place can be a control in another, and vice versa. This problem is difficult to avoid and plays a large part in explaining discrepancies between data generated by different laboratories.

The problem is partly historical in origin. Traditionally, medical researchers have almost always based their investigations on the presence or absence of a disease, of a symptom, of an environmental agent, and on the effect or non-effect of a drug or of a given treatment. These are all 'either–or' situations, and biomedical researchers have grown used to applying statistical methods derived from the so-called '2 2' analyses: presence or absence (2) of a marker tested against () presence or absence (2) of a disease.

Naturally, cholesterol level in the general population, being under multifactorial control, is a continuous variable (so are, for example, weight, height and blood pressure). The determination of a risk factor associated with a given level implies comparing the clinical manifestations associated with this level to those corresponding to a reference level (generally taken as 160 or 180 mg/dl): in other words, treating cholesterol levels as dichotomous (instead of continuous) variables. The value of determining relative risks, however, is to quantify an effect by a number with a concrete meaning.

The severity of atherosclerosis can be quantified only by coronary angiography. Occlusion by atheromatous plaques can occur anywhere, from one site in one artery to several sites in the three major coronary arteries. Furthermore, the thickness of the plaques is quite variable and is generally represented by percentage of arterial occlusion. Although there is no official definition of the sort that exists for the cut-off point above which atherosclerosis is considered an effective disease, several medical centres around the world regard subjects as patients if they are suffering from atherosclerosis when at least one major coronary artery is 40 per cent occluded in at least one site. This definition, accepted for lack of a better one, is open to debate. For one thing, I have always been fascinated by the black-and-white movie taken during the coronary angiography procedure: on a TV screen, you sort of guess the presence of some 2–3-mm-thick threads – the coronary arteries – constantly moving with each beat of the pounding heart. And a cardiologist can determine that one or more of these threads is occluded at 20, 30, 40 or 60 per cent by atheromatous lesions! The frontier between health and disease is very fuzzy indeed.

Separate laboratories involved in genetic-marker studies have often used different criteria for inclusion of subjects in patient groups. These criteria have consisted of either lipid disorder, myocardial infarction and documented atherosclerosis, or combinations of these three.

Some investigators have taken as patients groups of subjects with documented lipid disorders who have already suffered a heart attack. They reported that some RFLPs were more frequent among patients than among controls, and concluded that these RFLPs were high-risk markers for myocardial infarction. It was later argued that the RFLPs might actually have been protective markers. Their higher frequency among myocardial infarction survivors could have meant that they were associated with protective mechanisms against the effects of heart disease, and patients who did not have these putative mechanisms did not survive heart attacks.

The Paradox of Healthy Controls

One other problem concerning the design of experimental strategies based on the treatment of atherosclerotic heart disease as a split variable lies in the definition of controls. Of what is a control group composed? In theory, there should be only disease-free individuals from the same population as the patients, to whom they are age- and sex-matched. In the case of atherosclerosis, we simply cannot be sure that they are indeed not predisposed to the disease. Someone who is a control today can become a patient tomorrow. At the same time, his or her DNA molecules will have remained unchanged.

We do not know the state of the coronary arteries of individuals taken as controls. A definite answer would require performing systematic coronary angiographies, which is not feasible. Who would agree to undergo such a surgical procedure just to be considered a control subject in a research experiment? Besides, the cost of such a project would be too high. In this respect the usual terminology is wrong when applied to these studies. 'Control' groups should rather be labelled 'comparison' groups, bearing in mind that the designation is a temporary one. These people may be neither normal nor proper controls.

The advantage of working on genetic testing is that DNA is stable over the lifetime of a person: genetic markers are always the same. That means that, although it defies conventional experimental strategies, there is no need for age-matched controls. Indeed, compared to a fifty-five-year-old patient affected by coronary heart disease, a ninety-year-old person who is still in good health and has no personal or family history of heart disease and lipid disorder is a better 'control' than a corresponding fifty-five-year-old control (who might later develop atherosclerotic heart disease). And it is perfectly fine to compare DNA molecules of these two individuals, because the ninety-year-old person's genetic material is identical to what it was at fifty-five.

The nature of a chronic, degenerative disease is to increase in severity with age. Therefore, studies focused on a particular age group are of limited value and the results cannot be extrapolated to other ages. What should be carried out are more elegant, experimental strategies including subjects of all ages (ranging, say, from five to ninety-five), with varying degrees of severity of the disease. This way the investigator does not have to decide arbitrarily who is a patient and who a control. What will come out, however, are panels of genetic markers associated with either of the two extremes: high-risk markers always present in the more severely affected subject, and protective markers in the least affected individuals. Such procedures allow more extensive data analyses; they are derived from what is known in statistics as survival analysis. The hard part is to get hold of enough clinically well-characterized subjects to cover an age span as large as possible. The number of subjects required for a satisfactory analysis increases in proportion to the number of clinical manifestations to be included in the test.

The Way to Develop Genetic Tests

Patients and controls constitute a major resource required for the development of genetic tests. DNA probes constitute another fundamental resource. Molecular geneticists have the choice between two different approaches to determine the chromosomal locations they wish to study: targeted and random.

A targeted approach involves probing areas of the human genome that are known or felt to be implicated in disorders underlying atherosclerotic heart disease. Scientists take advantage of the knowledge gained from clinical investigations. Since the deposition in the inner wall of arteries of blood-circulating lipids is central to the process of atherosclerosis, a targeted approach for the study of molecular mechanisms involved in the development of the disease consists of studying those genes whose products are involved in lipid biochemical pathways. Quite a number of potential gene products belong to this category, and we know barely a fraction of them. Apolipoprotein genes are the most obvious candidate genes, and it comes as no surprise that they were used in most of the initial programmes.

A random, or comprehensive, approach is based on the isolation of random DNA fragments from cDNA or genomic libraries and the use of these fragments of unknown function as hybridization probes to detect RFLPs. This method, which is part of the general area of 'reverse genetics', has been nicknamed the 'brute force' approach. The degree of association between these randomly generated RFLPs and the phenotypic manifestations of atherosclerotic heart disease can be determined in extended, multigeneration families (linkage studies) or in samples of unrelated, diseased individuals (association studies) – the relative advantages of each approach have been discussed already.

The best way to identify genetic markers indicating an individual's genetic susceptibility to atherosclerosis would be to use random approaches combined with linkage analysis. Ideally, scientists should follow the transmission of the whole map of the human genome in a large number of extended families affected by various forms of atherosclerotic heart disease. However, this is not practical, as it would require just too much work and too much money.

Limits of Today's Molecular Genetics Research

The message is that both patient and comparison groups need to be well defined so that we can see precisely with what the corresponding genetic markers are associated. As of today, no scientist can pretend to have studied correlations between genetic markers and atherosclerotic heart disease. At best, some genetic markers have been found associated with some (known or unknown) variables of certain subtypes of atherosclerotic heart disease. The various research projects carried out so far amount to pilot studies and the preliminary data they have generated need confirmation from larger samples.

Maximum efficiency in these studies comes from the inclusion of the largest possible number of clinical variables. In the case of cardiovascular disease, scientists should be searching for associations between genetic markers and medical information on atherosclerosis, but also on hypertension, diabetes and obesity. These three afflictions certainly constitute risk factors for atherosclerotic heart disease, but they are also separate clinical entities with their own hereditary components. Development of DNA tests to identify their chance of affecting a person would be the first step towards adequate prevention.

Hypertension: The Silent Killer

Blood pressure is expressed in terms of corresponding pressure exerted by a column of mercury. It increases with age and, as for cholesterol levels, clinical epidemiologists have defined upper values beyond which a subject is said to be affected with hypertension; the blood pressure of a middle-aged person should not exceed 140/90 mm mercury. A person's blood pressure results from the effect of a combination of genetic and environmental factors; what is inherited is a genetic susceptibility to hypertension. It is generally admitted that, compared to atherosclerosis, fewer genes control the mechanisms regulating blood pressure. In this respect, it should be easier to identify the major genes implicated, because their effect is more important: they are probably more penetrant. Salt-rich diets, stress and personality factors are considered to be the main environmental components that contribute to a rise in blood pressure. Although 15 per cent of the population is considered to be hypertensive, we still do not know the cause of essential hypertension, the form of hypertension occurring in 95 per cent of cases. There are no specific symptoms directly attributable to hypertension, which is detected only through routine medical examination or because of its complications. These can affect the nervous systems (stroke), the eye's retina, the heart and the kidneys. Because hypertension remains symptomless for so long but ultimately has drastic consequences, it is called the silent killer.

Diabetes

Diabetes is a clinical syndrome characterized by hyperglycaemia, or elevated blood-sugar levels. It is caused by lack of insulin, a sugar-regulating hormone produced by particular cells (the beta-cells) of the pancreas. There are two major types of diabetes. Insulin-dependent diabetes mellitus (IDDM, also called Type I or juvenile-onset diabetes) is most frequent among people who are less than fifty years old and requires continuous insulin treatment. Non-insulin dependent diabetes mellitus (NIDDM, or Type II diabetes) affects middle-aged and elderly individuals. In its more serious forms NIDDM is compatible with an irregular insulin treatment. The overall prevalence of diabetes in the general population is 1 per cent. Susceptibility to diabetes is genetically inherited, but we still do not know how genetic and environmental factors interact.

Obesity

Obesity is not a disease; it is a symptom. Although plumpness has been appreciated during some historical periods and in some cultures, today the slim and fit look is seen as desirable. Modern medicine, together with statistics from insurance companies, is here to prove that a normal weight contributes to better health and a longer life. Apart from the case of rare organic illnesses, being overweight is due to overeating and a lack of physical exercise. Any weight excess represents an overload for the body and can be associated with cardiovascular disease, liver and gall-bladder disease, diabetes, bone and joint malfunctions, and aggravated osteoporosis – quite a list! Studies of identical twins separated at birth have revealed that the role played by heredity is even more important than was once suspected.

Intricate Interplay Between Risk Factors

The interaction between all of these afflictions is striking. Obesity, for example, is intimately associated with atherosclerosis, hypertension and diabetes. The clinical presentation of their symptoms is so intricate that medical researchers have long suspected the existence of common pathways for the four clinical entities. This means that one or several gene products participate in common biochemical and physiological mechanisms.

Where We Stand Today

Genetic-marker studies should help to resolve and identify these various mechanisms. Molecular geneticists are working now to develop genetic tests for all four afflictions. They are also hoping to find a battery of markers that will represent the overall effects of all these risk factors in the onset of cardiovascular disease. Such research programmes require DNA samples from large families in which complete clinical information on atherosclerotic heart disease, hypertension, diabetes and obesity is available for all members. Finding such ideally characterized families is the current limitation of these studies.

Historic Perspective

My own efforts towards the development of genetic tests for susceptibility to atherosclerosis started at the beginning of 1983. I had just taken a position with California Biotechnology Inc., a new biotechnology company located in Mountain View, in the heart of Silicon Valley. I had moved there from the department of Human

Genetics at the University of Michigan Medical Center, where I had spent two years as a post-doctoral fellow in the laboratory of Donald L. Rucknagel. I had worked on the molecular genetics of inherited haemoglobinopathies, or diseases caused by defects in haemoglobin molecules.

To me, moving into multifactorial and polygenic diseases was a challenge because it introduced another level of complexity. The field was new at the time, except perhaps to a small number of scientists. Yet the feasibility of unravelling the mysteries of atherosclerosis and other complex diseases seemed within arm's reach. We were now approaching the problem from the view of genetic susceptibility, and there was so much to discover.

Another research team at California Biotechnology, as well as two other American groups, had isolated the gene coding for apolipoprotein AI, the major constituent of HDL particles. The goal was to produce the apolipoprotein AI protein by genetic engineering and to use this molecule as a cholesterol-clearing, recombinant DNA drug. Today this scenario might seem naïvely simple and we know that it would never work in practice; eight years ago it seemed worth trying. At the time I had started other projects, but since the gene was available as a DNA probe, we decided to look for genetic markers at the apolipoprotein AI gene location. At first we wanted a small-scale study to check fairly quickly whether genetic markers at this genetic locus correlated with clinical manifestations of lipid disorders. In particular our aim was to identify RFLPs indicative of depressed apolipoprotein AI levels, and therefore of types of atherosclerosis due to decreased HDL. Little did we know that this locus would become one of the most studied by countless research teams from all over the world.

We had designed and equipped a complete laboratory to isolate DNA probes and identify RFLPs with maximum efficiency, and my research team quickly discovered ten RFLPs at and around the apolipoprotein AI gene location. What we needed were DNA samples from clinically well-characterized subjects. In other words, we needed scientific collaborators from major medical centres prepared to provide us with patient blood and DNA samples.

Fruitful Cooperation and the Proof of a Hypothesis

California Biotechnology's major asset from the very beginning was one of its directors and founders, John Baxter. As well as working at the company, he is a professor of biochemistry, biophysics and medicine, and the director of the Metabolic Research Unit at the University of California San Francisco Medical Center. He is famous not only for his contributions to medical and scientific research but also for knowing personally everyone worth knowing in these fields.

In 1983 John invited Gerd Assmann to the company for a couple of visits. Among other things Gerd is the head of the Cardiovascular Research Centre and of the Lipid Disorder Laboratory at the Westfälische-Wilhelms University in Münster, Germany. He is one of the world's experts on atherosclerosis. By 1984 we had decided to embark on an important scientific collaboration, and one year later we had found a panel of about thirty RFLPs at several DNA locations, including the apolipoprotein AI gene locus and other genes whose products were known from clinical evidence to be involved in the process of cardiovascular disease. We checked all RFLPs from that panel in 200 unrelated DNA samples from patients whose clinical histories (including information about lipid and lipoprotein values, incidence and family history of myocardial infarction) were on file in Münster.

In August 1985 I went to Münster for a few days, taking with me the list of genetic markers determined in the first series of 200 subjects. We entered this data into the main-frame computer of the Lipid Disorder Laboratory and looked for possible associations between RFLPs and clinical variables. Immediately the computer print-out revealed several positive correlations between some of these RFLPs and some clinical values.

We knew, of course, that we would find a certain level of positive correlations, a phenomenon due to the nature of statistical analyses, which take into account a certain 'significance level' called the p-value; because of this value, 5 per cent of the total number of associations studied in our analysis were expected to have positive correlations. This is due to chance alone and has no real significance. Our results, however, greatly exceeded the 5 per cent level of positive associations, which meant that several of these correlations were real.

We knew at this point that we were on to something extraordinary. The methodologies developed by molecular geneticists were shown to be applicable to the determination of genetic susceptibility to multifactorial disorders. This is accepted today and researchers apply the techniques to several disorders with genetic factors. A few years back, however, the theory behind our experiments was in its infancy and was emerging only with the preliminary results.

I went back to California Biotechnology with the raw data and analysed it carefully. It became clear that we had discovered a panel of five RFLPs that could serve, in the sample population used in our pilot study, as genetic markers indicating a higher risk of developing a heart attack. These results were preliminary and required confirmation in larger samples from other populations; they were a mere scratch on the surface. But their fundamental impact was to show us that we were heading in the right direction. Our basic hypothesis was true, the method had worked and we had even found high-risk markers where we had expected to find them. We had raised a corner of the curtain hiding a scene that will take years, or even decades, to play.

John Baxter and I, in agreement with the marketing department of the company, decided to send out a press release to coincide with my presentation of these results at a symposium on atherosclerosis organized by Gerd Assmann in Münster at the end of October 1985. This press release had the effect of a bomb when it hit the newswires. Newspapers, magazines, TV and radio channels all gave us extensive coverage and pushed us into an area we knew nothing of at the time – press interviews.

Wall Street analysts were particularly keen to hear about the prospect of new-generation genetic tests; they saw in this line of work a good sign for the company's future. On the other hand, they may have felt personally pleased to learn about improvements in the fight against heart disease. Around the time of the press release, the company's stock price went up from $9 to $14 a share. Afterwards they followed a favourable up-turn of the whole market and benefited from a temporary unconditional faith in the general field of biotechnology on the part of investors; the share price had climbed to almost $30 (the highest it ever went to) by 1986. In several media articles, and in particular in *Business Week*, California Biotechnology was referred to as a 'genetic-marker company', even though the project based on the development of genetic tests was at that time one of fourteen that were under way in the company.

Representatives of the American Heart Association stressed the importance of this type of work in the battle against cardiovascular disease. Extensive coverage in the media, as well as in scientific and medical literature, contributed greatly to make the public aware of the validity of genetic-marker studies and to have them recognized by people who still doubted their real potential. These ideas gained such wide acceptance that even California Biotechnology's staff begun to think that the project was worth it after all.

This was not the first report of its type. In 1982 a Danish team led by D. Owerbach had published an article in the *Lancet* in which they described a possible association between genetic markers at the insulin gene locus and coronary artery disease. Owerbach had previously worked in Bill Rutter's laboratory at the University of California San Francisco Medical Center on the molecular biology of the insulin gene. Insulin is mostly known for its role in the mechanisms of glucose regulation, but it is also a major hormone controlling the mobilization of triglyceride by the various cells of the organism. It was thus not surprising that Owerbach and his group had looked for associations between the insulin gene and clinical manifestations of lipid disorders. Although they were later granted a patent on this work, at the time they did not receive the attention warranted by their report. Interestingly, we also confirmed the presence of high-risk markers for atherosclerotic heart disease at the insulin gene locus in our experiments on the German DNA samples.

By 1985, when we made the press release based on our data, several other groups were actively working on similar projects. Overall, the publicity we received had the beneficial effect of making it easier for us to find potential collaborators. I received phone calls from many investigators at a variety of medical centres who were interested in starting joint ventures. I was pleased by this turn of events, because I had been aware from the very beginning that these studies would require major collaboration: not only blood and DNA samples from thousands of clinically well-characterized subjects but also additional DNA probes from all over the human genome would ultimately be required. We were now ready to start moving in the right direction.

There is another reason why these studies need to be carried out in several different sample populations. As if there were not enough problems already, individual genetic make-ups themselves throw up additional difficulties. RFLPs that are good markers for a particular clinical entity in one population may not be so in a different population. In terms of gene-marker frequencies, genomes have diverged among various ethnic groups. Ideally, the validity of good markers should be proved to exist across ethnic barriers. This needs to be demonstrated by experimental evidence, which means checking DNA samples from individuals from geographically distinct populations.

Worldwide Collaboration

Between 1985 and 1988 the list of our scientific partnerships was growing constantly. We started working with John Laragh and Steven Atlas (Hypertension Center, Cornell University Medical Center, New

York); Ernst Schaeffer, José Ordovas and Jean Genest (Atherosclerosis Research Center, Tufts University and Boston University Medical Center, Boston), who also had access to the subjects from the Framingham Study; Ernesto Salcedo and Herbert Naito (Cleveland Clinic); Charles Glueck and Denis Sprecher (University of Cincinnati School of Medicine); John Kane (University of California San Francisco Medical Center); and a major Japanese pharmaceutical company in association with three medical centres from Japan.

Of course, there has also been a lot of stimulating competition from several research teams located mostly in America and Britain. The laboratories of Jan Breslow (Rockefeller University, New York), Mike Brown and Joe Goldstein (Texas University, Dallas) and Ray White (Howard Hughes Foundation, University of Utah, Salt Lake City) have been the most active over the years in America, and those of Steve Humphries, James Scott, David Galton and Bob Williamson have led the way in Britain.

Although these studies represent a huge amount of work, an increasing number of laboratories from all over the world have decided to take up the challenge. There is a tacit understanding among molecular biologists: DNA probes isolated by a research team are made available to other groups which ask for them (sometimes with restrictions as to their proposed use). My laboratory has received hundreds of requests for the dozens of probes we have isolated. Most concern probes suspected to be involved in the processes of cardiovascular disease. We have sent them all over America and the European countries, but also to the USSR, the People's Republic of China, Singapore, Saudi Arabia, Cuba, Puerto Rico and Argentina.

The development of genetic tests to determine an individual's susceptibility to heart disease represents such a massive effort that it should be pursued in a spirit of worldwide cooperation between laboratories. We should now move beyond the stage of pilot projects and begin in a major way large-scale programmes to identify definite panels of genetic markers used in genetic testing. These programmes should be monitored by an organization of representatives from several countries designed on the model of HUGO, the human genome organization.

Scientists, however, need to set up reasonable priorities that can serve the purposes of all areas of molecular genetics. One of the short-term goals of the genome projects, for example, is the elaboration of both a complete cartography and a physical map of the human genome. These are prerequisites for carrying out efficiently a comprehensive study of a complex disease such as cardiovascular disease, for which most of the major gene effects are still unknown. Today the focus of most experts in molecular genetics is monogenic diseases. DNA tests for these can be elaborated very rapidly, and their studies serve as acid tests before getting into multi-factorial disorders. Methodologies for data treatment and analysis are now being drastically improved, and experimental procedures will be speeded up with the introduction in research laboratories of automated equipment. With the advent of the genome projects, the study of cardiovascular disease using gene-marker technology is becoming more feasible every day.

Towards the Future

The current state of research in the general area of genetic markers and cardiovascular disease is that we know the methods of molecular genetics can be successfully applied to the identification of an individual's genetic susceptibility to a polygenic disease. Where is this leading us?

The long-term goal of these programmes is in line with the concerns of other biomedical disciplines. Researchers are looking for better means of controlling atherosclerotic heart disease and reducing its toll with effective treatment modalities as well as with preventive measures.

Genetic testing aimed at detecting an individual's predisposition to heart disease should ultimately be applied as early as childhood so that all appropriate measures can be taken in time – before the disease starts its progression. These measures should be more specifically tailored to individuals who are at higher risk because of their genetic make-up.

The development of DNA tests is indeed but a first step towards winning the race against disease. Once genetic markers have been found to correlate with atherosclerotic heart disease, scientists can use the techniques of chromosome walking to reach the chromosomal location of and identify defective genes. They can then determine the DNA abnormalities responsible for the various symptoms of the disease, thereby arriving at a better understanding of the process of cardiovascular disease. But this is no easy task. It will take time, effort and money. In fact, finding all the major genes involved in the mechanisms of cardiovascular disease is such a huge undertaking that some scientists still believe that it is impossible.

An understanding of the genetically controlled pathways leading to heart disease represents in turn a springboard towards the development of appropriate therapies adapted to the specific causes of the disease. This, however, is debatable. The power of biotechnology to elaborate therapeutic agents for treating the roots of afflictions discovered with the methodology of reverse genetics is still very limited. But we should not underestimate its potential. Advances are made every day even though, to the general public, they may appear very slow. We have every reason to be optimistic, for we now have the basic knowledge and the equipment with which to explore further.

8

Cancer and Heredity

THE WORD 'CANCER' CONJURES UP PICTURES OF A FUTURE OF DARK
abysses leading inescapably to a grim and painful death. Cancer
is the disease we fear the most. Not only does it seem to strike
at random but, because we hear so much about it, its frequency in
the general population seems to be on the increase all the time.

Cancers of all types represent the second-highest cause of mortality
in industrialized nations, right after cardiovascular disease. One
quarter to one-third of the population dies from some type of
cancer. Yet we try desperately not to think too much about it,
and somehow, by almost denying its existence, hope to be lucky
and escape the fate of the unfortunate victims who are picked off
one by one.

Even when we are enjoying perfect health, we still think of cancer
as the most terrible death sentence, yet this is unfair, because cancer
is no longer a death sentence. Science and medicine have come
together to shape new weapons for the battle against an enemy
that we have now chased out of its hiding-place. Today, doctors
treat or cure about 60 per cent of all cancers. Twenty-five years
ago all patients who had leukaemia died; today two-thirds of them
conquer their illness and survive.

Despite encouraging results, however, we are also seized by
doubt, and we have legitimate reason to fear that doctors are far
from mastering cancer. Indeed, the general public is reluctant to
acknowledge the hope shown by statistics. Hopelessness is exacerbated by recurrent apprehension that few practical applications have
come from all the fantastic research, that major discoveries remain
confined within the boundaries of research laboratories.

It is just that techniques developed in research centres around
the world take time before becoming concrete measures applicable
in hospital wards – not because doctors are lazy or inefficient, but

because, for the patient's sake, these methods have to pass stringent tests before approval by competent authorities.

In fact, we have every reason to be optimistic about progress made in both the early detection and the treatment of cancer. Improvements of conventional methods, as well as the arrival of genetic engineering in biomedicine, are contributing to raise our hopes.

The three major fields involved in the treatment of cancer are surgery, radiotherapy and chemotherapy. Extensive refinements in these areas have coincided with the emergence of new types of therapies, such as photodynamic therapy and thermotherapy. As for early detection, scanner, echography, mammography, fibre optics and NMR (nuclear magnetic resonance) permit the visualization of smaller tumours, the lower size limit of which is now in the order of 0.5 cm. But it is the advent of molecular biology and molecular immunology which gives real hope for a quantum leap in the management of cancer on three fronts: detection, treatment and cure.

With ever-increasing accuracy scientists are identifying risk factors and even genes playing leading roles in the onset of the disease – invaluable knowledge which brings the promise of revolutionary forms of treatment. We estimate that by the end of the century, dozens of new-generation drugs will be available to contain, treat and cure cancers. Anti-growth factors, anti-cell-proliferation agents and anti-cancer genes will trigger a radical change in our control of the illness. Detection of an individual's genetic predisposition with the help of genetic markers and immunological tests will provide the ultimate sensitivity in early detection. We will then be able to predict many types of cancers before their onset.

The combination of early detection and new therapies follows the general tendency towards predictive and preventive medicines, which are of particular value when applied to cancer. Indeed, the earlier the detection, the greater the chances for success.

Widespread information and education among the public at large have had positive results in that people are more prone to have frequent check-ups. In the Western world anyway, it is now unusual for patients to see a doctor because they have a tumour the size of a fist on their cheek.

Gene therapy is another method we will have to count on. Today scientists are able to induce *in vitro* transformation of a cancer cell into a cell which reverts back to almost normal. The next step is to move from *in vitro* to *in vivo* reversion of cancerous cells.

So, science and medicine do their share in the battle against cancer. But all advances will be of limited value if they are not paralleled with modifications in the individual's life style. Once again alcohol, tobacco and bad eating habits are culprits that need strict control.

What Is Cancer?

Our body is an assemblage of 60,000 billion cells representing a dynamic system where information is constantly exchanged in the form of chemical messengers. To ensure the smooth running of biochemical reactions characterizing life's processes, the body produces and stores energy, which is later spent on specific functions performed by different tissues. The heart pumps blood into blood vessels; lungs exchange blood gases with the atmosphere; red blood cells carry oxygen and carbon dioxide; the liver and digestive tract participate in food digestion; muscle contraction permits various types of movements; thought processes take place in the brain, where nerve centres also control all activities of the organism; and bones provide a solid physical frame.

Most of the cells in our body grow and divide all the time – which is obvious if you think of the passage from babyhood to adulthood, of hair growth and of a wound healing. In fact, the following example is sufficient to illustrate the extraordinary liveliness of our bodies at the microscopic level. Bone marrow, a blood-cell reservoir, produces 4 million cells each second. Cell division means manufacturing DNA, and when we sum up the total number of cells dividing every day, we realize that about 300 million miles of new DNA are thus synthesized – the distance between the earth and the sun!

What is euphemistically referred to as 'the biological clock' of the organism controls cell division and growth. When the machinery is perfectly tuned, the right number of cells divides at the right time. As mentioned earlier, however, the replication system responsible for synthesis of new DNA makes a few errors. The extraordinary efficiency of repair mechanisms corrects over 99.9 per cent of all mistakes, but still a few remain. This explains the existence of genetic variations in DNA molecules. The average mutation rate is extremely low – in the order of one in 10 million – but it rises with the effect of chemicals (mutagens) and radiation.

While many DNA variations are of no consequence for the fate of the organism, a few of them can introduce modifications in proteins participating in the mechanisms of regulation of cellular division and differentiation – proteins that are part of the biological clock. As a result, the corresponding cells escape control and start proliferating in an anarchic manner. They become deaf to regulatory signals sent by other organs. These cells have acquired the property to grow and develop independently. They have become cancer cells – parasites taking precedence over their hosts. Naturally, because the abnormalities affect DNA molecules, the acquired cancerous behaviour is transmitted to all daughter cells, which explains the continuous growth of the insidious tumour.

Many different factors can induce random cell proliferation, to the point where we can consider each cancer as a particular disease. Indeed, even a given, specific cancer type manifests itself differently in different patients. There are differences in severity, in the time of development and in the time between the first symptoms and the actual onset of the cancerous growth. In fact, the progression of a cancer follows a slow course and involves many different stages. Up to fifty years can separate the acquisition of pre-cancerous characteristics and the true development of the cancerous tumour. This explains why the risk of suffering from cancer increases with age. Centuries and even decades ago, the same older people may have had similar odds of getting cancer, but they would probably have died from one of the many infectious diseases then fatal before being affected by their rampant cancer.

Cancer can affect any cell and any organ. As with cardiovascular disease and allergy, cancer is not *a* disease, but a heterogeneous group of disorders whose end – random cell proliferation – is the main common feature. Cancer is thus a general term encompassing many disorders, each being triggered by several causes – a multifactoriality including genetic, environmental and psychological stressors.

Cancer, by Any Other Name . . .

Discussions about cancer often confuse terminology. There are two main reasons for this: the first is psychological and the second, patho-physiological.

First, people hate to talk about cancer, especially when they are directly concerned. Traditionally, patients have refused to accept the very idea of their illness, as have their families, who do not dare mention the illness openly. Furthermore, doctors in many countries have become used to hiding the severity of the disease from their patients; not so long ago the word 'cancer' was forbidden in many oncology wards. We have come a long way since those days and now realize the part open dialogue with patients and their families has to play in the success of treatment.

Still, the general unwillingness to mention the word 'cancer' has resulted in a widespread use of euphemisms. It is common, for example, to use cancer and tumour interchangeably. This is wrong. A tumour is a general term designating a non-inflammatory growth. While some are malignant (cancerous), others are benign (non-cancerous).

Second, cancer bears different names in medical terminology, depending on what part of the organism is affected. A melanoma, for example, is a malignant tumour made up of melanin-producing cells: that is, specific cells of the skin. A carcinoma is a malignant tumour formed from epithelial tissues; a sarcoma, from conjunctive tissues; a blastoma, from embryonic cell types. Leukaemia is a blood cancer characterized by white-blood-cell proliferation. On occasion I have heard acquaintances talk about cancer patients, saying, 'Thank God, it is not cancer; only metastases!' A metastasis is a cancer cell moving from one part of the organism to another, where it settles and triggers another cancer. Metastases are responsible for the common picture of cancers appearing in different parts of the body.

This happened to an uncle of mine, who was diagnosed at fifty as having cancer of the jaw. A large portion of his jaw was removed surgically and he was treated with radiation therapy. Six months later, he started to suffer from sharp back pains and he was operated on for a slipped disc. During the operation, the surgeon realized the truth. My uncle did not have disc problems, but many tumours all along his spine. The extent of tumour proliferation was so high that it was useless at that point to attempt any form of treatment. He died a couple of months later.

A similar thing happened to Chris, who one day, at the age of thirty-three, noticed what he thought was a mole on his ear. He consulted a dermatologist, who diagnosed a malignant melanoma and found another one on Chris's back. Both observable melanoma were surgically removed. Four months later, Chris experienced a lower back pain radiating to his legs, and thought he had trouble with his sciatic nerves. Upon closer examination, he was found to be suffering from generalized cancer of the spine. He and his wife were talking about 'a few tumours and some metastases' while cheerfully organizing a celebration party for the day he was to leave the hospital. They went on refusing to accept the truth until the very day of Chris's death.

It is true that chances for a cure tend to decrease with an increasing number of strikes, but this is not always the case and there are many success stories to soften the harshness of this general rule. Amy suffered breast cancer at the age of forty (treated by radiotherapy), lung cancer at forty-four (treated by chemotherapy), and cancer of the lumbar vertebrae at forty-nine (removed by surgery). She is now over sixty, in good health and enjoys a 'normal' life away from hospital wards. If a cancer is not cured right away, a period of between two and fifteen years' remission (depending on the size of the tumour at the time of treatment) is necessary for the cancer to be considered definitely cured. As a rule of thumb, however, doctors assume that a patient is safe after a ten-year remission period – more than the time elapsed since Amy's last cancer episode.

A Cultural Disease

Different types of cancers strike different parts of the world. It all depends on individual and on population ways of life; in particular, on an individual's genetic susceptibility to certain cancer types, and on exposures to various cancer-causing agents.

The world leader is indisputably lung cancer. Each country, however, has its own champions: liver cancer in the People's Republic of China, as well as in African and South East Asian countries; stomach cancer in Japan; colon, breast and prostate cancers in America; colon and breast cancers in the UK.

The best preventive measure against cancer is to eliminate the exposure to cancer-causing agents. It does not come as a surprise to hear that 80 per cent of all bronchi and lung cancers are caused by tobacco and that half of all cancers could be prevented if tobacco and alcohol were cut out. Although everyone knows about the deleterious consequences of these two products, people still continue to smoke and drink excessively. Several reasons come to mind to explain this paradox. First, emphasizing the damaging effects of alcohol and tobacco has become such an old cliché that people have stopped listening. Then, to modify one's life style is a difficult thing to do, especially when it comes down to dropping substances that provide instant gratification. Not to mention that both alcohol and nicotine are real drugs for which the user develops an addiction. There is also the psycho-analytical theory which sees excessive drinking and smoking as passive methods of suicide. The recurrent remark, 'My doctor smokes, so why should I stop?' is still heard, though it is a poor excuse.

As with cardiovascular disease, we know that attempts to change an individual's way of life are a waste of time. Rather it is society's perception of alcohol and tobacco that needs to change. In Britain and America massive anti-smoking campaigns have succeeded in presenting smoking as an outdated and filthy habit, which constitutes a powerful stimulus for many people to stop. Still, statistics indicate that heavy smokers keep on smoking as much, if not more, than before. The cigarette industry represents too much money at too many levels to disappear suddenly. But manufacturers are aware of the danger and have started to invest in other fields (Phillip Morris, for example, developed in the 1980s a passion for soft drinks).

Methods of Treatment

The three traditional methods of cancer treatment are surgery, radiotherapy and chemotherapy. All three constitute a 'brute force' approach, but nevertheless they have considerable success.

The surgeon's role is to remove the tumour, and the great challenge is to take out all cancer cells, otherwise the tumour grows back again.

Radiotherapy, or radiation therapy, consists of sending radiation of several kinds to strike and kill the tumour. Doctors are concentrating on the introduction of new types of radiation which avoid burning healthy tissues and destroy the tumour accurately and specifically. Hence the advent of neutrontherapy.

The principle of chemotherapy is to treat the disease with anti-cancer drugs. These are toxic chemicals that block specific stages of cell division by preventing DNA replication. Ideally, they should specifically kill cancer cells and spare the normal cells of the body. Scientists have tested millions of such chemical compounds and have selected a battery of about fifty. Patients generally receive cocktails composed of a few of these anti-cancer drugs.

Chemotherapy makes it possible to cure patients in a state of advanced cancer proliferation. At the moment, however, it has two major drawbacks. First, toxic molecules display a restricted spectrum of action; their efficiency is variable, and depends on the cancer type, because they attack different tumours with different degrees of aggression. And second, they affect all cells of the organism. Lethal doses for tumour cells are toxic for normal, healthy cells; they even kill normal cells that grow too fast. Hence the presence of adverse side effects associated with chemotherapy, such as hair loss, nausea, fatigue, diarrhoea, loss of appetite, weight loss and muscle cramps. The use of portable pumps permits the dose to be regulated and also the delivery to be targeted to those precise times of the day associated with maximum efficiency.

Photodynamic therapy is a hybrid method using both chemotherapy and radiation therapy. Injected chemicals kill the tumour when activated by light. This method is warranted only in the case of tumours located 2 cm under the skin at the most, because of the poor penetration of infra-red radiation.

Other techniques have been developed over the years and have been associated with some success in certain cases. Such is the case of thermotherapy. We have known for a long time that an increase in temperature kills cancer cells. Indeed, tumours that are poorly irrigated because they lack appropriate blood-vessel networks cannot clear out heat as well as the cells from normal tissues. The idea is thus to heat up a tumour with the help of an electromagnetic field in order to kill progressively the cancer cells.

However, the greatest hope for the early detection, treatment and cure of cancer lies with molecular immunology and molecular biology.

Natural Defence System of the Organism

In our body the immune system is in charge of exterminating all foreign cells and substances. This defence mechanism is composed of many cell types, the most frequently talked about until now being B and T lymphocytes. B lymphocytes produce a class of protein called immunoglobulins, also referred to as 'antibodies' because they recognize exactly and bind to molecules – the antigens – against which they have been synthesized. The extraordinary plasticity of the gene complex coding for immunoglobulins allows the synthesis of one particular antibody directed against each antigen entering the body, so that every antigen gets tagged with a label signifying 'to be destroyed as fast as possible'. T lymphocytes are responsible for the identification and destruction of foreign cells thus marked with an antibody for elimination.

Several other types of cell ensure an efficient line of defence against intruders. Scientists have given particular attention to these because of their potential usefulness in the therapy of diseases caused by the undesirable effects of foreign substances. Among these other cell types, macrophages, K and NK (killer and natural killer) cells, LAKs (lymphokine-activated killer cells) and TILs (tumour-infiltrating lymphocytes) top the list of ones that have been shown to play an important role.

Immunology is the study of the organism's response to various types of aggression by foreign bodies, and is thus directly implicated in unravelling the pathways leading to cancer and in finding new treatment modalities for the disease. Indeed, a cancer cell exhibits abnormal characteristics; without even getting into the internal mechanisms disturbing cellular regulation, a cancer cell is different both in size and in shape from its normal, non-cancerous counterpart. Cancer cells should thus be recognized as foreign to the body and destroyed. Yet they manage to escape the tight control exerted by the immune system.

A cancer progresses step by step, sometimes spanning, as mentioned earlier, a fifty-year period, often as a two-stage event – first, the appearance of a benign tumour, and, second, the later development of a real cancer. The body should thus have the time and opportunity to get rid of the abnormal tumour. Yet this does not happen. The reason for the failure of the immune system to perform correctly remains unknown. However, a great hope in the panoply of treatment modalities is to boost up the seemingly lazy or dormant part of the immune system, and especially the very cells whose role is to destroy cancer cells. This general strategy belongs to the field of immunotherapy.

One way of eliminating a given tumour is to inject massive doses of a patient's own lymphocytes. Since, however, the lymphocytes have not performed their initial role, doctors first need to activate them – to train them to be operational so that they can complete their mission. Scientists have gained the power to achieve this task with natural hormones isolated from the organism's own defence system and whose function is precisely to activate the various cells of the immune system. This is the case with interferons and interleukin-2.

Interferons belong to a family of substances produced by different cells (alpha-interferon is synthesized by blood cells; beta-interferon, by fibroblasts; gamma-interferon, by T lymphocytes). They act as natural drugs involved in fighting parasite and viral infections, auto-immune diseases and cancers. They are, of course, not appropriate for all cancers, but because they stimulate NK cells they work best in the case of kidney cancers, melanomas, the AIDS-associated Kaposi sarcoma, chronic myeloid leukaemia and hairy-cell leukaemia (a form of leukaemia in which cells appear hairy upon observation through a microscope; there, interferon acts as a hormone regulating the growth of leukaemic cells, and thus prevents rather than cures the disease).

Interleukin-2 is a hormone which serves as a growth factor for B and T lymphocytes as well as for NK cells. It is of particular value against kidney and skin cancers, some types of lymphomas and some leukaemiae.

The therapeutic approach consists of isolating a patient's own LAKs and TILs, so that they can be cultured and multiplied *in vitro*. After activation with, for example, interleukin-2, the cells are then reinjected to the patient. This technique certainly offers tremendous possibilities, but, as with any other method, it is also associated with toxic side effects, including fatigue, fever, water retention and in some cases myocardial infarction. We have laid the foundations for this form of therapy, which we know is a successful one. What we need now is to be able to carry out a fine-tuning in order to dampen the side effects while reaching a greater accuracy.

We have known for a long time that the immune system plays a role in the fight against cancer. At the end of the last century doctors noticed spontaneous ameliorations in cancer patients affected with severe bacterial infections. Since then, many attempts have been made to treat patients with injections of various bacteria. This has always had mixed results. It could never be entirely satisfactory, because there is no direct cause and effect relationship between the bacterial infection and the amelioration of cancer symptoms. It is just that the bacteria stimulate the immune system, and that the awakened lines of defence sometimes fight cancer cells as well. Successful cases have thus been lucky hits over which we have had no real control. However, the technique of immunotherapy as developed over the past few years is a new-generation approach which enables us to target our attacks with greater accuracy.

For a few years now, there has been much talk about immunotoxins as effective therapeutic agents. An immunotoxin is a synthetic molecule resulting from the combination of a powerful toxin with an antibody directed against a given tumour. The mode of action of this complex is conceived as a two-step process. First, the antibody looks for and binds to its specific receptor (its antigen) located on the surface of tumour cells. Second, the toxin that it carries enters the tumour cells and kills them. This is what should ideally happen. In practice, however, experience has uncovered two major obstacles standing in the way of success. First, the physical structure of some tumours limits the action of immunotoxin molecules. Indeed, large and solid tumours benefit from low blood supply, so that their centres are difficult to reach, thereby escaping the action of the drugs. And second, the specificity of antibodies for their corresponding antigens is not quite perfect, which introduces a major toxicity problem, because antibodies bind to other, normal cells as well, and thus target these for destruction by the toxins. Scientists are actively working at improving this technique, but so far they have obtained fewer positive results than originally expected.

At present the introduction of gene-cloning technology in the field of immunology is the source of great excitement. After much debate the news finally came through in July 1990 that Steve Rosenberg and his team had been granted approval by a special panel of experts convened by the Recombinant DNA Advisory Committee of the

NIH to investigate a new line of treatment for advanced malignant melanoma. One of the functions of TILs is to attack cancer cells building up into melanomas. The presence of an advanced melanoma in a patient indicates that TILs have not performed their role well enough to destroy the tumour. They can, however, be made to work more efficiently towards that end. Rosenberg's team proposed to remove patients' TILs and insert TNF genes into these (TNF, for tumour necrosis factor, is a protein which kills tumours by preventing them from developing adequate blood-supply networks). They then grew *in vitro* billions of the TNF-transformed TILs, and injected them into the patients to attack the melanomas. By autumn 1990 their first results indicated that the conditions of half the treated patients had improved.

Genetic Predisposition

Cell growth escaping control; cell division going haywire; altered or missing regulatory proteins. Now we are back to the DNA molecule again, for it orchestrates all these functions. This is why molecular genetics is of great value for understanding the mechanisms leading to cancerous transformation. The techniques of molecular biology also allow us to envisage different ways of detecting, treating and even curing cancer.

Cancer is neither contagious nor a genetic disease. As with cardiovascular disease, it follows a complex model of inheritance. A small number of cancers, however, are transmitted according to the classical laws of genetics. We estimate that hereditary forms of cancer represent 2 to 5 per cent of all cancers. These include retinoblastoma (cancer of the retina, affecting young children); Wilms tumour (a kidney cancer); medullary thyroid carcinoma, a cancer of the thyroid gland (the thyroid is an endocrine gland, located at the base of the neck in humans, which produces thyroxin, an iodine-containing hormone involved in the regulation of growth and metabolism); and xeroderma pigmentosum, a type of skin cancer appearing in areas of the body exposed to sun.

Most forms of cancer, however, are associated with an individual's genetic susceptibility. We have known for a long time that cancer runs in families. The higher the susceptibility, the higher the risk of developing the same cancer as other members of the family. Less serious genetic predispositions are marked by the development of different types of cancer among different family members. The vast majority of cancers are the result of multifactorial considerations, including genetic and environmental factors, and also mutations occurring during the life of an individual. We can thus assimilate cancers to acquired genetic diseases that are not transmitted to the offspring. The goal of current research in this field is the development of tests allowing the determination of an individual's genetic predisposition to cancer.

Such a research programme involves the identification of genes whose products play a role in the onset of the disease. Many candidate genes can be advocated to fit this criterion. The most obvious are genes directly implicated in cellular growth and differentiation. Upon various types of modifications, which occur as a result of copying errors and of mutations following the action of cancer-producing chemicals (carcinogenic compounds) and of radiations, such genes become capable of inducing cell proliferation. These particular genes are called oncogenes (from the Greek *onkos*, tumour).

There are two different classes of oncogenes – proto-oncogenes and anti-oncogenes – and their actions are antagonistic. Indeed, we know today that the regulation of cellular growth and division is under the control of two opposite mechanisms – an activation of the system ensured by proto-oncogenes coupled with an inhibition resulting from the action of anti-oncogenes. The process of development of a cancer necessitates two events taking place in conjunction: gain of an activating function realized by the transformation of a proto-oncogene into an oncogene (generally as a result of a mutation), and loss of an inhibitory function when the corresponding anti-oncogene is deactivated by loss or mutation.

Other genes play a role even though they do not participate directly in the onset of cancerous properties. These include genes whose products participate in the process of DNA repair and in the degradation of chemicals entering the cell. In the latter case, the risk arises from the accumulation of toxic substances generated by chemical degradation, which can induce mutations at the DNA level.

Proto-oncogenes and Anti-oncogenes

The general definition of an oncogene is a gene whose modification or overexpression causes directly one of the steps of the cancer process.

Proto-oncogenes do have a natural function in the organism, as they participate in the process of cell division. They were originally discovered in cancer-causing viruses such as Roux sarcoma virus, a virus causing cancer in chickens. The peculiarity of these viruses is that they are RNA viruses, meaning that their genetic material is constituted by RNA molecules instead of DNA molecules. How, then, do they manage to multiply? When they infect a host cell, they give orders to the cell to synthesize an enzyme called reverse transcriptase, whose function is to copy RNA back into DNA. The newly manufactured DNA molecule – exact copy of the virus's RNA – gets integrated into the host cell's genetic material. Scientists have discovered fifty such viruses, each carrying a particular oncogene. They made an intriguing discovery when they realized that our DNA molecules also contain oncogenes. They called these cellular oncogenes to differentiate them from viral oncogenes. Cellular oncogenes similar to all reported viral oncogenes have been found in human cells. In fact, all living organisms contain cellular oncogenes in their genetic material. Since their structures have been extremely well preserved throughout evolution, we know that oncogenes play a fundamental role in cell division.

One of the first characterized proto-oncogenes, called c-myc, for example, has been shown to play an active role in cell division occuring during the first stages of embryo development. Indeed, injection of an antibody directed against c-myc (therefore inactivating it) in a batracian egg stops any further division; its precise role, however, remains unknown. In humans, the measure of myc expression represents a prognostic factor for some cancers, and especially cancer of the uterus. When the c-myc gene is overexpressed in the cells of an early tumour, the odds of developing another cancer later in life are eight times higher than when the gene expression is normal.

The accuracy of tests based on measuring oncogene expression, or on identifying oncogenes, is not quite absolute. Indeed, in the case of colon cancer, for example, a mutation occurring in the proto-oncogene c-ras is present in only 60 per cent of all cases – which also indicates that different genes can be at the origin of the same type of tumour. Still, a targeted method of treatment for colon cancer could be a drug against the protein encoded by the oncogene c-ras.

Determination of an individual's genetic susceptibility to cancer consists of identifying DNA variations responsible for the conversion of a proto-oncogene into an oncogene. Such a test, however, is complicated by the fact that it generally takes the action of several oncogenes (from two to seven) to develop a tumour. Moreover, scientists have to include in the test DNA variations causing an inhibition of the action of the corresponding anti-oncogenes.

The very existence of anti-oncogenes counteracting the effects of oncogenes had been suspected for a number of years. It was demonstrated in 1986, when scientists reported the isolation of the Rb gene, an anti-oncogene whose inactivation causes retinoblastoma.

Retinoblastoma is a malignant tumour developing from immature retinas of small children (the retina contains pigments with which we see shapes and colours). This monogenic, recessive disorder affects one out of 15 to 30,000 births. The treatment is efficient in over 90 per cent of all cases, provided that the diagnosis is made early enough. It is, however, a drastic one, because it involves removing both eyes by the age of one or two, with subsequent radio- and chemotherapies. A higher risk remains, however, of developing other types of cancer, especially breast cancer, osteosarcoma (bone cancer) and at least one type of lung cancer. Retinoblastoma is due to the loss of the anti-oncogene Rb (which is located on the long arm of chromosome 13) in both alleles. It follows a simple hereditary transmission in 40 per cent of cases. Generally, one defective Rb gene is inherited from one parent, and another mutation or deletion occurs in the cells of the retina. Alteration of both genes in the DNA of one cell leads inevitably to the development of a tumour. If only one allele is affected, there is an increased risk of developing a tumour in the retina, as well as in other parts of the body. With the use of an Rb DNA probe, scientists have been able to make a genetic test for detection of retinoblastoma. This test can be used prenatally.

The demonstration that the Rb gene is an anti-cancer gene was made when it was shown that the introduction of one Rb gene in the genome of a cancer cell induced an *in vitro* reversion to a normal state.

Anti-oncogenes block the cancerous proliferation induced by onco-genes. We believe that anti-oncogenes corresponding to all oncogenes, to which they look very much alike, exist. The anti-oncogene corresponding to the c-ras oncogene was characterized in 1988 by a French team working with the genome of the fruit fly, and in 1989 by a Japanese research team working on the human genome. This anti-oncogene, called respectively rap and Krev-1, codes, as the oncogene c-ras does, for a G protein. G proteins constitute a class of protein binding to guanosine triphosphate. They play a role in the transduction of information across cellular membranes and in the cell. The G proteins encoded by c-ras and Krev-1 may act in an antagon-istic manner on a control protein not yet identified. This seems, however, the most likely explanation for their mode of action.

The use of anti-oncogene products as anti-cancer drugs appears as a very promising form of therapy. Alternatively, another targeted approach would be gene therapy. The anti-oncogenes inhibiting a given type of tumour could be cloned into vector viruses that would then introduce them into the tumour cells.

Early Detection and Prevention

A young mother is diagnosed as being affected by a medullary thyroid carcinoma, the hereditary form of thyroid cancer. While she is successfully treated, her three children are immediately put under medical surveillance. The younger one shows an increased blood level of calcitonin, a hormone whose levels become elevated in the case of thyroid cancer. The surgeon decides to operate, and he indeed discovers a minute tumour, which he immediately removes. A few years later, the younger child is fine. This true story illustrates the value of family history for making a prognosis of the disease.

Prognostic tests and early detection are prerequisites for conquering cancer. One goal of biochemical research is to expand the available battery of tests in order to implement more preventive medicine. Identification of oncogenes and anti-oncogenes falls right into this general strategy. Once an individual's genetic susceptibility is established, preventing the onset of the tumour is often possible with the management of associated environmental factors. Closer medical supervision of individuals at higher risk also permits the early detection of any cancer type, and therefore allows successful treatment to start in time.

We know the benefit of frequent check-ups and of simple, routine medical examination in the detection of various cancers, such as breast, cervical and prostate cancers. Yet the public still need to make adjustments in their attitude towards the acceptance of preventive measures.

One of the best preventions and most effective therapies is to talk openly of the disease. Raised awareness about all aspects of cancer, as well as life-style modifications such as decreased alcohol and tobacco consumption, decreased sun exposure and added fibre in the diet, are all necessary measures which, luckily enough, seem to be regarded as acceptable by society at present.

9

Rashes, Coughing, Sneezing and Laboured Breathing: The Price of Allergies

SUE IS SITTING ON HER BED IN A CAREFULLY CONFINED HOSPITAL ROOM, devouring a novel. The book rests into a tight and rigid plastic box. She turns the pages with the help of rubber gloves whose wrist end is sealed on to the front side of the box. This whole device has been devised for people like her, for whom reading could prove a fatal passion. Sue is so allergic to both paper and printing ink that exposure to either one could simply kill her.

Allergies are expressed in many different ways. One person can immediately become pale when in contact with flour, and start shaking, sneezing and feeling a burning sensation in the eyes. A hairdresser who is allergic to a particular solvent found in a cosmetic product experiences sudden difficulty in breathing: filled with anxiety, he or she runs to open the window in order to get some fresh air. In another person, soap leaves red, itchy patches all over the skin areas that have been washed. Then there are the more common hay fevers, sneezing episodes or asthma crises suffered by many people who are in the vicinity of grass, flowers, dogs and cats.

The Many Forms of Allergy

Allergy is not a disease. As with cardiovascular disease and cancers, allergy is an ambiguous term that encompasses several types of immune reactions leading to a multitude of pathological states of varying severity. Allergies are triggered by the activation of mechanisms implicated in a type of immune response known as immediate hypersensitivity.

When a foreign molecule, compound, body or parasite (the antigen) enters the body, it triggers a cascade of defence mechanisms from that particular part of the organism, among which a crucial reaction is the recognition and binding of the antigen by a specific antibody. A molecule provoking an allergic reaction is a type of antigen known as an allergen.

Allergies manifest themselves in different clinical symptoms. Asthma is often an allergic respiratory disease, characterized by difficulty in breathing, chest constriction, coughing and wheezing sounds. We used to think that it was the result of a direct bronchoconstriction (narrowed bronchi); in fact, narrowing of bronchial airways is due to muscle contraction and muscle spasms. This first effect is then followed and aggravated by an inflammatory response. Bronchi muscles are extremely sensitive: they respond in an exaggerated manner to various chemical mediators and to irritants from the environment. There have been many documented epidemic outbreaks of asthma throughout the world. In 1987, for example, allergens found in soya beans combined with pollution were responsible for an epidemic of asthma in Barcelona.

Allergic rhinitis results from contact of the nasal mucosa (mucous membrane) with breathed antigens. Several symptoms follow, such as nasal congestion, watery nasal discharge and sneezing, causing irritation. Allergens typical of rhinitis are grass pollens, provoking hay fever. They also include pollens from many grass varieties, flowers and trees, as well as dust.

Allergic eczema is a non-contagious skin inflammation characterized by scaly patches and itching. Children during the third month of life often present some forms of allergic eczema spread over cheeks and head. These forms develop with remissions, and can then heal spontaneously at about five years of age. However, babies and children with allergic eczemas often suffer from respiratory allergies, and particularly from asthma, later in adulthood.

Urticaria is marked by small swellings and rednesses on the surface of the skin. These weals and flares generally appear shortly after eating food containing the culprit allergens and are due to local dilations of capillaries. They disappear within one to three days and leave no visible marks on the skin.

Food allergies can induce digestive symptoms such as diarrhoea and vomiting, or more systemic reactions (reactions affecting the whole body), such as urticaria and eczema. These effects develop within minutes to hours following ingestion of the offending food allergen.

The most serious allergic form is a condition known as anaphylaxy, or anaphylactic shock, commonly prompted by bee and wasp venoms, certain drugs and certain foods. Usual inflammatory symptoms such as redness and oedema (swelling) appear first, for example, at the point of stinging. This uncomfortable, although minor, condition can sometimes quickly lapse into a sharp aggravation such as suffocation accompanied by severe hypotension (a sudden, important, drop in blood pressure). Death results from hypoventilation, followed by lack of blood oxygen, culminating in cardiac arrest.

The diverse forms of allergies are generally reversible in children, and they disappear progressively. In adults, however, allergies represent definitive conditions with a tendency towards aggravation, either in the severity of a particular allergic response or in sensitivity to a greater number of allergens.

Common allergies are uncomfortable rather than serious conditions. Allergic individuals can live and perform very well.

Allergens and Allergy-Causing Factors

In ten years, between the 1970s and 1980s, the incidence of asthma increased by 30 per cent and skin allergies more than doubled. Incriminating factors lie in modifications to our environments and our modes of living. Every day new chemical compounds and new types of food become widely available, some of which constitute powerful allergens for certain individuals. Over 200 chemicals used routinely in factories provoke marked allergic reactions. Allergies are also more common among active, inner-city inhabitants.

There are so many different molecules throughout the world that it does not come as a surprise to learn that everybody is allergic to something to varying degrees. While some people have allergies so mild that they go almost unnoticed, others suffer greatly, from tolerable rhinitis or ephemerous urticaria to severe asthma and anaphylactic shocks, with all possible combinations in between.

Many products contain compounds that represent allergens for a small number of people only. Universal allergens do not exist. In our current state of knowledge, it is impossible to predict who will be allergic to what, which is a major problem for food and pharmaceutical industries. Indeed, all products, be they synthetic or organically grown foods, cheap or expensive cosmetics, synthetic or natural drugs, are bound to trigger an allergic response among a certain number of people.

Overall, we have to recognize that food allergens are extremely rare compared to the amount of products that we eat. Food allergy can also be difficult to differentiate from food intolerance. Some ethnic groups, for example, display a genetic deficiency for an enzyme called lactate dehydrogenase, whose function is to participate in the degradation of milk products. Practically, individuals with a lactate dehydrogenase deficiency cannot digest milk because they suffer from a hereditary intolerance – not from an allergy – to milk. Nevertheless, food products yield a particularly rich crop of allergenic items: fish and sea food, strawberries, apples, pears, apricots, celery, carrots, milk and eggs are but a few of those which top the list.

The three most common allergies are due to pollens, domestic dust and pets. Pollens are little particles that contain the male reproductive cells of flowering plants. Ragweed pollens cause hay fever, or seasonal rhinitis, an acute and marked irritation of the upper respiratory tract and the eyes. Pollens from grasses, flowers and trees all provoke different forms of allergies. The incriminating allergens in domestic dusts are microscopic animals, of which scientists have identified 36,000 species. The Pacific island partly constituted by Papua New Guinea was untouched by this form of allergy until the introduction of allergen-containing blankets triggered an outburst of these dust allergies. With cats and dogs, it is not the sight of the animal which is responsible for an allergic reaction, nor – as commonly thought – the hair, but a protein found in the animal's saliva that gets deposited on its hair when the cat or the dog licks itself.

Bird feathers also contain allergens. Metals such as cobalt, nickel, chromium, as well as plastic and rubber, are the source of eczemas. Isocyanate paints, widely used for car bodies, induce severe asthma among many workers.

At home cosmetics, perfumes, soaps, cleansers and insecticides cause various allergic reactions – and so do wasps and bees. During the first days of a holiday, sun exposure often produces, besides the inevitable sunburn, mild to severe allergic rashes all over the body except the face.

Common allergens are thus everywhere and a list of them would go on and on. We will close it here with medical drugs. Indeed, probably one person out of ten is allergic to some drugs, the most allergenic ones being antibiotics, especially penicillin.

Innate and Adaptive Immune Systems

Scientists and physicians have made much progress in understanding the mechanics of allergies with the development of immunology and, more recently, with advances prompted by the fast pace of biotechnology.

Immunology was originally developed as a scientific discipline studying resistance to infectious diseases. It soon appeared that the organism has a natural defence against infectious invasions, and that outbreaks of infectious episodes do not affect everybody; some are more resistant than others. The innate immune system is the first, immediate defence mechanism of the body against foreign agents such as viruses, bacteria and parasites of all kinds. The scavenging role is performed by specialized white blood cells that literally eat and destroy the pathogens.

A more subtle and sophisticated process involving learning and memory on the part of the organism's immune system is called adaptive immunity. Each foreign molecule entering the body induces a unique reaction targeted towards its specific destruction. Specialized white blood cells called lymphocytes somehow remember all compounds that they have encountered so that they are always ready to prevent their subsequent action. The AIDS virus is very active and efficient because it simply inactivates a category of lymphocytes known as T lymphocytes, thereby rendering inefficient the whole natural defence system.

Upon subsequent contact with a provoking antigen, certain people develop a dangerous hypersensitivity to this antigen; this marked reaction is what is referred to as 'allergy'.

Today immunologists' main line of research is the study of this hypersensitivity at the cellular and biochemical levels. Molecular immunology applies to the investigation of the genes coding for protein implicated in immune responses and allergies.

Allergy, an Imbalance of the Adaptive Immune System

The adaptive immune system involves the activation, proliferation and transformation of B lymphocytes, which secrete the antibodies directed towards the antigens. These antibodies are proteins called immunoglobulins (Ig). Each of the billions of molecules and pathogens that invade the body is recognized by a particular Ig. This simple observation gives a general idea as to the complexity of Ig combination, organization and manufacture.

When an antigen (for example, ragweed pollen) enters the organism for the first time, it is immediately recognized as a foreign substance by the organism – a parasite that must be destroyed. To do this, B lymphocytes transform into plasmocytes, producing a specific Ig belonging to a class of Ig known as IgE. These liberated IgE tag on to receptors located at the surface of other cells that play a key role in the allergic reaction – blood basophils and tissue mastocytes. Either one of these two types of cell can be solicited; which it is depends on whether the reaction occurs in a particular tissue (nasal mucosa, bronchi, digestive tract, uterus, skin) or affects the whole organism.

When the allergen comes back a second time, it binds to the existing IgE, which stimulates the corresponding basophils or mastocytes. These cells in turn secrete molecules called chemical mediators, which have very powerful effects on vasodilation (increased capillary size), bronchoconstriction (narrowed bronchi due to the constriction of blood-vessel muscles) and chemotactic functions (they attract other types of scavenger cells). Scientists have already discovered over fifty chemical mediators, among which we find histamin, heparin, leukotriens and prostaglandins, as well as new classes of proteins whose study has been made possible with the development of bio-technology; these include platelet-activating factor (PAF), cytokins, interleukins, interferons and tumour unecrosis factor (TNF).

The destruction of one antigen by one antibody is thus a performance involving complex and diverse reactions, and is played by numerous leading actors: cells of the immune system (B and T lymphocytes), key cells of allergic reactions (blood basophils and tissue mastocytes), inflammatory and scavenger cells (eosinophils, neutrophils, monocytes, macrophages, platelets) and over fifty known chemical mediators of the inflammatory response.

The complexity of immune reactions is a marvel of accuracy and sophistication. It reveals, once again, the extraordinary fine-tuning ability of the body. Interrelated mechanisms whose role is to guarantee the defence of the organism against foreign compounds are constantly and precisely controlled. This dynamic system functions in an equilibrium where fluctuations are tolerated within a certain physiological range of activity. Beyond a certain point, however, the system lapses into a pathological hypersensitivity characteristic of allergic reactions that display varying degrees of severity and can sometimes go as far as cardiac arrest and the ensuing death of the organism.

Why Some People Are Allergic and Others Are Not

Why do some people become ill when in contact with pollens while others remain unaffected? This is because an allergic reaction is a multifactorial syndrome resulting from the interplay between environmental, psychological and hereditary factors.

The environment plays a dominant role. First of all, the allergen is typically a substance of the environment, and the process leading to exposure of the allergen is massively influenced by the environmental context. Pollution, smoking, trauma of the respiratory system and viral and microbial infections bring out the effects of the allergen. Physicians have often observed that a viral infection sensitizes the respiratory tract and paves the way to ragweed allergy among patients who show a predisposition to hay fever. Similarly, the risk of developing an allergy is much higher among children of parents who are both smokers.

Despite considerable debate and speculation on the subject, nobody has yet been able to define an allergic personality. Psychological stressors, however, exert a major influence; they can aggravate and even trigger an allergic response. Back in 1886 physicians reported that fake roses could trigger severe asthma episodes among patients who were allergic to rose pollen. Similar cases abound, and literature and painting fans will be interested to hear that Marcel Proust was seized with serious asthma when looking at van Gogh's *Sunflowers*. Many people who are allergic to cat's or dog's saliva proteins suffer from violent rhinitis or asthma episodes when they see a cat or a dog on their TV screen.

Parents of an asthmatic child who, understandably, live in fear of the next asthma episode, can transmit their anxiety to the child, and tension is often one of the causes of the much dreaded attack.

Besides environmental and psychological considerations, the part of genetic factors in the onset of allergies is also well documented. Allergies, as with cardiovascular diseases and cancers, run in families, and epidemiological studies have clearly demonstrated the influence of a genetic predisposition. Here again, because of the complexity of the underlying phenomena, the precise mode of transmission is unknown; we cannot call upon genetics to tell us who will suffer from what type of allergy.

Contact with an allergen induces excessive syntheses of IgE, whose overall production in the organism is under the control of a recessive mode of inheritance (it involves the presence of two gene effects located on two homologous chromosomes). The production of specific IgE, manufactured by the adaptive immune system and targeted towards specific allergens, is under the control of the human leukocyte antigen (HLA) system. HLA are unique identity numbers located on the surface of white blood cells. They allow the immune system of an organism to recognize the self from the non-self. With the innate and unique characteristics represented by the HLA system, we enter the complex world of specificity of recognition. As we have seen already, it is vital for an organism to identify, recognize and eliminate as quickly as possible all foreign and abnormal cells, including various infectious agents as well as cancer cells. For surgeons the HLA system represents a major problem in the case of organ grafts, for these are truly foreign to the body (unless the graft has been isolated from a twin).

The genetics of the HLA system is probably one of the most difficult to understand because of the system's complexity. The complexity of the HLA system is also responsible for causing a marked reduction in both sensitivity and specificity of diagnostic tests based on the use of the system's components. This means that results are never clear-cut. For example, the odds of developing ragweed allergy among carriers of an HLA gene called DN3 are 90 per cent, against only 25 per cent in the rest of the population. That is probably the best result yielded by molecular immunology. It cannot, however, be applied as a routine screening test, not only because of the uncertainty but also because other triggering factors play a role in the onset of hay fever.

Observations such as presence of DN3 are nevertheless very useful for prevention because we can then start the identification of putative higher-risk individuals whose progress can be closely followed. Because of the number of variables, their respective complexities and also the fluctuations in the importance of triggering factors, scientists cannot at this stage apply the techniques based on the use of classical genetic markers, as they were able to with sickle cell anaemia, Duchenne's myopathy and cystic fibrosis.

Diagnosis of Allergies

Given the extraordinarily large number of substances that everyday life exposes us to, the identification of an allergen can be a difficult and time-consuming task. The first step is to fill out a questionnaire. From the preliminary hints provided by the answers to specific questions, the physician carries out sensitivity tests to check the allergic reaction. These tests are also called prick tests, because a minute amount of the many allergens to be tested are individually pricked under the skin of the patient – generally in the arm and shoulder – with a fine needle. The allergenic substance induces a positive reaction at the corresponding prick spot, characterized by the appearance of local swelling (a weal and flare) within minutes of its deposition.

When doubt still remains, the next step is the provocation test, in which the patient is made to inhale increasing doses of the suspected compound until there is manifestation of the allergic response.

Since one of the main reactions in an allergic response is increased secretion of IgE, an obvious method is to measure the amount of IgE

present in the serum. This is done with more sophisticated immunological tests. Total IgE concentration, for example, is determined
with a RIST (radio-immuno sorbent test). We have to take into
account, though, that the value of IgE concentration varies with
age and sex. Besides, although IgE concentrations are generally
high among allergic individuals, false positives as well as false
negatives are frequent. It means that individuals with high IgE
are not all allergic, and that some allergic patients have low serum
IgE concentrations. Nevertheless, newborns with family histories of
allergy who have high serum IgE concentrations have a much higher
risk of developing an allergy of one form or another before the age
of six or seven.

RISTs have already been refined, so that sophistication is paralleled
with better specificity. In a few cases, the concentrations of particular
IgE that are specifically directed towards certain allergens can be
determined with another radio-immunological method called RAST
(radio-allergo sorbent test).

Treatment of Allergies and Promises for the Future

Allergy is yet another example of a multifactorial syndrome marked
by a host of complicated and diverse reactions. Classical and
molecular immunology, as well as biotechnology, contribute to
our understanding of the processes involved, offering promises
about the development of new types of drugs tailored to specific
manifestations of allergies.

The complexity of allergic reactions, however, means that it is
unreasonable to think that we will be able to cure an allergy by
blocking a single step of the process. We must not build up false
hopes – as certain biotechnology companies have done – because
for the moment no imminent revolution is foreseeable, no miracle
drug that will enable us to treat all patients. Instead, current research
applications extend the list of efficient drugs already available.

As with heart disease, hypertension or cancers, the same general
strategy for fighting allergies exists: first, prevention, and, second,
the use of specific drugs appropriate to each particular case.

The best form of therapy – prevention – meets common sense:
allergic patients should avoid any contact with the allergen. In cases
such as Sue's, suppression of the causing agents (paper and printing
ink) is vital; provided that books are carefully sealed to avoid direct
contact, Sue can continue to read for as long as she wants. Most
cases are not as serious, and it is often sufficient for a person who
is allergic to grass pollens to seek cover when a neighbour mows

the lawn. Pollen calendars for lawns, wheat, corn and rice are available and patients allergic to any of these can avoid walks in the countryside during periods of high pollen counts.

Likewise, workers who present a hypersensitivity to isocyanate paints should avoid working in a body shop. For practical reasons, however, these sorts of decisions often mean making a sacrifice in one's life style, or ability or even field of specialization. Having to move to another job when there is no other alternative can be painful for someone living in an area where unemployment is high.

Environmental factors cannot always be controlled. In the 1960s a couple moved to the desert region of Phoenix, Arizona, because the husband suffered severe hay fever. He was fine and had no further trouble until grass was introduced to the region. They had to move again to another dry area, hoping that grass would not follow them a second time – which it has not so far.

Desensitization is a long-term form of treatment that once carried much hope but has brought mainly frustration. The aim of desensitization is to block IgE production by injecting at regular intervals increasing, minute doses of allergens – a form of vaccination against allergy. There are two major problems. First, it can aggravate, rather than alleviate, the symptoms of some patients. And second, it works only in an unpredictable manner in 40 to 60 per cent of all cases. For these reasons, and because success or failure seems random, the method has been dropped in several countries, but considerable effort is being made to understand and control the factors governing success.

Drugs are currently manufactured by chemical synthesis. They act at different levels of the chain of allergic reactions.

Asthma is controlled with bronchodilators such as beta-mimetics and xanthin bases.

A good way to avoid an allergic reaction is to prevent the release of chemical mediators from the key cells of allergic reactions – basophils and mastocytes. This is the typical action of sodium chromoglycate, used as a preventive agent. Reduction of the inflammation caused by the secretion of histamine and other mediators is well achieved by typical anti-inflammatory agents such as corticoids (cortisone and its derivatives). Corticoids would be ideal forms of treatment if it was not for their numerous adverse side effects.

Another category of drugs acts at the end of the chain of chemical mediators. Anti-histamines, for example, inhibit the binding of histamine to its specific receptors; tissues thus become insensitive to the action of histamine. Until now, a major side effect associated with anti-histamines was drowsiness, but new forms do not induce this any more.

The size of the market for the treatment of allergies acts as a strong catalyst, prompting severe competition among conventional pharmaceutical and biotechnology companies. Prospects for high investment returns contribute to a rapid development of new drugs with increasing efficiency and specificity. Research on anti-PAF is a good example of on-going investigation.

PAF (platelet-activating factor), a chemical mediator, is a phospho-lipid produced by different cells in the lung, heart, skin and kidney. Active at very low doses and extremely powerful, it activates most inflammatory cells and induces asthma. Compared to the action of histamine, which is treated as a gold standard for inflammation, PAF is 1,000 times more active as a factor of platelet aggregation; it also exerts a potent effect on bronchoconstriction. Although it was discovered in 1972, it was not until the early 1980s that the identification of its structure and its chemical synthesis paved the way to research on antagonists to counterbalance its effects.

Chemical compounds with anti-PAF effects were discovered and characterized in 1984 in the form of gingkolides, which specifically inhibit the binding of PAF to its receptors. Gingkolides bear their name because they are isolated from the leaves of *Gingko biloba*, a living fossil according to Charles Darwin himself. It appeared 200 million years ago and it is probably the most ancient living tree. The Buddhists treat it as a sacred tree, and people from the Far East have known for thousands of years that leaf extracts have the virtue of calming asthma. Because their chemical synthesis is too difficult (and therefore too costly), the extraction of gingkolides is realized from leaf cells grown in laboratory cultures. Scientists have gone on to discover additional anti-PAF compounds in various trees, moulds and bacteria.

A lot of emphasis is put on the development of anti-PAF substances, because they have a wide range of activities, and consequently offer a large spectrum of medical applications. Besides treatment of allergies, they can be used for improving graft survival, as anti-oedema agents (oedema is caused by infiltration of fluids in tissues), as inhibitors of ischaemias, as agents decreasing mortality caused by burns and also to decrease the nephrotoxicity of xenobiotics.

Other important research efforts are concentrated on the manu-facturing of leukotrien antagonists and interleukin inhibitors.

Molecular immunology brings its own tools for the development of medications for the next generation. Two general strategies seem to have promise. The first consists of producing only the part of

IgE molecules that binds to the receptors, and to use these parts as agents binding to and saturating the receptors. They would compete with natural IgE, in the sense that there would be no room left for the IgE produced by the organism on the surface of their target cells. The second idea is to engineer a complex molecule formed by the addition of a toxin to isolated IgE molecules, so that when the IgE binds to mastocytes, for example, the toxin would inactivate or kill the cells, thereby preventing them from secreting chemical mediators. In the current state of knowledge, however, these ideas still require a lot more work before they yield useful products.

Finally, we should conclude with a word on more esoteric forms of treatment. Acupuncture, herbal teas, homoeopathy and chiropractic are constantly advocated as methods of treating and even curing allergies, and indeed they have all been associated with amelioration of symptoms in some cases. Until proved otherwise, we have to accept that the improvements are due to placebo effects: that is, observed effects triggered by a substance or an action having no demonstrated medical property and administered for its psychological effects. We should not, however (as purists tend to do), discard the virtues of psychological factors – especially in the case of allergic responses. After all, if psychological stressors can trigger allergies, why not accept that they can also reverse their effects? With a syndrome such as allergy, where the part psychological factors play is undeniably powerful and for which there exists no miracle treatment, we need to include every tool possible in our efforts to improve the patient's condition.

Are We All Destined
To Be Old and Demented?
Alzheimer's Disease Provides a Clue

WHEN I JOINED CALIFORNIA BIOTECHNOLOGY IN 1983, I STARTED working on the automation of some procedures routinely used in molecular biology and on developing cholesterol-lowering drugs by gene-cloning technology. Soon after I also became involved in developing prognostic tests to detect an individual's genetic susceptibility to heart disease.

The research scientists in the company were always actively looking for new research projects which were feasible from a scientific standpoint and also made sense commercially. Among my proposals I remember three which were briefly considered. One was to design an anti-inflammatory agent for ulcerative colitis (inflammation of intestinal walls) which could be taken orally. The second consisted of engineering a molecule which would inhibit the normal action of the enzyme pancreatic lipase, which degrades lipids within the digestive tract; the dietary lipids would no longer be digested and would be prevented from entering into the blood vessels. The third one concerned coupling vitamin B12 to a transport protein so that the vitamin B12 would be rapidly absorbed by the stomach wall; such a compound would be useful in treating pernicious anaemia, a form of anaemia due to vitamin B12 deficiency.

The costs of these projects, the equipment that would be needed, the market research suggesting profits would be much less than $1 billion (the management was very greedy at the time) and the availability of existing competitive drugs with similar effects were some of the reasons which made us decide not to try these projects.

Since my laboratory was designed to handle genetic-marker studies, I recommended that we undertake programmes to develop diagnostic tests for other hereditary diseases. Some of these ideas were approved by the company's management. But when I suggested a genetic test for schizophrenia, the executive scientific committee looked at me as if I was out of my mind.

'Schizophrenia is not even a genetic disease!' I was told.

One of the other scientific directors put the palms of his hands forward in a gesture which meant that maybe in a century or two one could reconsider this proposition.

Well, schizophrenia is a genetic disease. So are many other neuropsychiatric disorders – a conclusion that had already been demonstrated back in 1983 with the discovery of genetic markers associated with Huntington's disease. In February 1987 a paper published in *Nature* reported the existence of a gene located on chromosome 11 that predisposes the Amish community to bipolar disorder. In November 1988 another issue of *Nature* established that susceptibility to at least one form of schizophrenia is caused by one or more abnormalities of a gene located on chromosome 5.

Molecular genetics has had a major impact on the understanding of neuropsychiatric disorders. We are also beginning to be aware of the high frequency of underlying genetic traits in the general population. In this respect, Alzheimer's disease provides a good example of a mental disorder amenable to the techniques of biotechnology.

The Inevitable Toll of Alzheimer's Disease

Alzheimer's disease, once described as a separate entity in 1907 by the German physician Alois Alzheimer, is one form of senile dementia. For the past few years it has been much in the news, principally because of the progress made on the basic research front, in which molecular biology has played a pivotal role. Public opinion was made particularly sensitive to the problems of Alzheimer's disease after the death in her fifties of Rita Hayworth, at one time the ultimate glamorous actress. She had intelligence, fame and beauty, and yet she suffered the consequences of this devastating illness. Nobody escapes the ravages of this disease.

Alzheimer's disease is a chronic, degenerative illness which can start as early as the third decade of life. Typically, however, it manifests itself after the age of forty-five and the percentage of affected patients increases with age. Between 5 and 10 per cent of individuals over sixty-five suffer from some form of dementia, half of which is believed to be of the Alzheimer's type. Alzheimer's disease is another example of an illness that is more prevalent today than it was in the past. The reason, once again, is increased longevity. In America it affects about 2 million individuals and 100,000 patients die every year from its complications. Both men and women are equally affected.

The typical manifestation is impairment of short-term memory. Patients presenting the first symptoms of Alzheimer's disease will start to forget everyday routine acts, such as whether they have locked their front door or turned off the stove. They will have increasing difficulty remembering the names of common items, such as household objects. Little by little, they will lose their ability to speak and to take care of themselves, until they die from the complications of their dementia.

At this point I must add a word of warning. One needs to be cautious when collecting information to describe the symptoms of a psychiatric disorder. Reading about a disease tends to induce hypochondria. Whenever I read the DSM-III manual (1980 United States Classification), the most widely used textbook for making psychiatric assessments, I recognize some aspects of my behaviour in at least 80 per cent of the pages. It does not mean, I hope, that I display 80 per cent of all recorded mental illnesses. There are specific criteria for each of them that only a psychiatrist is able to evaluate. In my case, I know that I suffer from memory lapses and that I have the troublesome habit of losing both my keys and my identity papers, which has exasperated my family for quite some time. The diagnosis of my behaviour is not Alzheimer's disease, but simple lack of attention to items I consider unimportant.

Besides memory loss and its associated effects, Alzheimer's disease patients display anti-social behaviour (they become increasingly indifferent to their environment), tending towards aggression. What is often painful for carers is the lack of appreciation.

Once early symptoms of Alzheimer's disease appear, does this mean that a person will eventually reach a state of complete dementia? The unfortunate answer to this question is yes, even if the length of time this takes can vary: from first symptoms to death can take anything from five to twenty years, although the average time is typically seven to ten years.

Diagnosis of Alzheimer's Disease

The diagnosis of Alzheimer's disease represents a major problem, for it can only be done unambiguously by neuropathology techniques, which means taking brain samples and observing them under a microscope after specific staining. Only a post-mortem examination can certify that a patient had Alzheimer's disease. The neuropathological hallmarks of Alzheimer's disease are the presence in the brain of highly characteristic deposits called senile (or neuritic) plaques, of neurofibrillary tangles and of cerebrovascular amyloidosis. These correspond to a progressive loss of nerve cells (or neurons) involved in memory, cognition and thought processes. A correlation between concentration of senile plaques and severity of dementia has been documented.

Another observation gaining currency concerns the presence of aluminium. We have known for some time now that brains of Alzheimer's disease patients contain unexpectedly high levels of this metal. The results of a recent study published in the *Lancet* incriminate the high aluminium concentrations in drinking water and certain drugs. The disease is indeed more frequent (by a factor of 1.5) among people living in English and Welsh districts where the concentration of aluminium in drinking water is elevated – often by a factor of ten! Similar links between Alzheimer's disease and aluminium were also reported back in 1986, following an investigation in Norway.

Several programmes are under way throughout the world to determine exactly the role of aluminium in Alzheimer's disease and also to understand its toxic effects. The information obtained will be of the utmost importance, because aluminium is used in many industries, including food and drugs. It is found, for example, in drinking water and in drugs such as antacids and cough syrups. This awareness of its deleterious side effects will certainly pose a major problem of reconsidering its use in food and drug manufacturing and processing.

Only 60 to 80 per cent of patients showing symptoms of dementia end up being diagnosed as suffering from Alzheimer's disease. To reach this ambiguous diagnosis, several weeks of specific tests are required under in-patient conditions. Yet a differential diagnosis is useful to rule out other forms of dementia which can be either treated or handled differently.

Bleak Current Means of Treatment

In the case of Alzheimer's disease, there are no cures, no treatment, no way to slow down the progression of the illness. Our inability to treat Alzheimer's disease stands in stark contrast to the numerous possibilities of counteracting other degenerative diseases such as atherosclerosis. There, the deposition of cholesterol and other fats in arteries can be retarded, stopped and even reversed by diet, exercise and cholesterol-lowering drugs. There is nothing of this kind for Alzheimer's disease. Deposition in the brain of senile plaques and neurofibrillary tangles is an unstoppable and progressive process which will take its toll inexorably on the patient's mental state and life.

In desperation, many people have suggested that intellectual exercises could defer the continuous loss of neurons – a suggestion stemming from two demonstrable facts. First, neuronal activity is known to reduce neuronal death. And second, the death of nerve cells is compensated to some extent by a mechanism whereby the remaining neurons send additional extensions towards other neurons in order to consolidate the network of neuronal interactions. Neuronal death is not confined to Alzheimer's disease; it is the unavoidable hallmark of ageing. Nerve cells do not divide as other cells do. Not only do we not gain any, but we lose about 1,000 of them every day. This loss is accelerated by the effect of substances such as alcohol and monosodium glutamate (a flavouring agent used in oriental cooking), which act as true brain killers. In the case of Alzheimer's disease, though, mind exercises to counteract neuron depletion would be a drop in the ocean. We need to face the fact that Alzheimer's disease is characterized by major organic lesions which are, at the moment, irreversible.

Prospects for Genetic Testing

We need a reliable diagnostic test for Alzheimer's disease that can be easily performed and the most obvious candidate is DNA testing. A recently reported finding is worth mentioning in this context. Alzheimer's disease is associated with modifications not only in the brain structure but also in a part of the nervous system which is more readily amenable to examination: the olfactory epithelium.

This epithelium is composed of the nerve cells in the nasal membrane whose function is to recognize various smells. It is known that some patients suffering from Alzheimer's disease have an impaired sense of smell. The recent report has implicated characteristic pathological abnormalities in the neurons of the olfactory epithelium. Since these neurons can be grown under laboratory conditions, their detailed study will probably help us understand better the origin and the progression of the disease. If the abnormalities appear early enough in the disease process – as yet, an unknown – they could also be used for the detection of Alzheimer's disease in its early stages.

Pathological abnormalities in tissue that is easier to biopsy than the brain make for interesting leads that several laboratories are pursuing. It is clear, however, that Alzheimer's disease is hereditary.

We know this from twin, family and epidemiological studies. As such, it is amenable to investigation based on the techniques of molecular genetics, and what we hope to develop are DNA diagnostic (and prognostic) tests.

Two forms of the disease have been described: familial Alzheimer's disease and sporadic Alzheimer's disease. The familial form shows an autosomal dominant mode of inheritance: it is caused by one major gene defect (dominant), and the defective gene is located on one of the twenty-one autosomes (autosomal) and not on the sex chromosomes. We are not yet quite clear about the mode of transmission of the sporadic form but guess that it may be due to an autosomal dominant genetic defect with incomplete penetrance; other minor genes may then modulate the effect of the major one. However, we do not know whether the major gene defects are the same in the two forms of the disease. As a result of higher penetrance, familial Alzheimer's disease can be expected to occur at an earlier age, and it does. Its first symptoms typically appear around the age of sixty, although they sometimes manifest themselves as early as thirty-five. The overall clinical presentation and the neuropathological findings in both forms are otherwise identical.

Finding a genetic test for Alzheimer's disease involves identifying the gene responsible for the disease by using genetic markers to signal the presence of this altered gene. During 1986 and 1987 considerable progress was made in that direction: the location of one gene responsible for the familial form of the disease was identified. Since the disease shows an autosomal mode of transmission, we can eliminate the X and Y chromosomes. This narrows down the search, but colossal efforts are still needed. Where should we begin? In which one of the twenty-two autosomes and in which part of each of those? Here an important observation made things much easier. All patients with Down's syndrome, or trisomy 21 (these patients have three copies of chromosome 21 instead of two), display the characteristic brain pathology of Alzheimer's disease very early, by the age of forty. This suggests that some region of chromosome 21 must be involved in Alzheimer's disease.

James Gusella's team at Harvard University isolated random genetic probes from human chromosome 21 to detect genetic markers, which were then tested in several families affected by familial Alzheimer's disease. They made a discovery which confirmed what was suspected: some of these genetic markers, located at the beginning of the long arm of chromosome 21, were present in the DNA molecules of affected family members. This meant that the altered gene must be present somewhere in the vicinity of these markers. Scientists had the necessary proof. Familial Alzheimer's disease is a hereditary disease and, in the families used for these investigations, results from a gene abnormality located on chromosome 21.

Amyloid Beta Protein

In parallel with these studies, other investigations generated much excitement. Senile plaques consist of a mixture of axons and neurites surrounding a plaque core, which is itself made from the aggregation of a protein. This protein has had several names but is now commonly referred to as amyloid beta protein. This protein deposition correlates with the severity of dementia, so it was thought that maybe a defect there causes the chain of events leading to Alzheimer's disease.

Several laboratories isolated the protein, determined its amino acid sequence, inferred the corresponding DNA sequence of the encoding gene and finally isolated amyloid beta protein DNA probes from both genomic and cDNA libraries. These probes were used to determine the location of the gene. The surprise was that the amyloid beta protein gene was found to be located at the beginning of the long arm of chromosome 21. It was thus more than tempting to speculate that a defect of the amyloid beta protein gene was the cause of Alzheimer's disease.

An amyloid beta protein genetic probe had been isolated at California Biotechnology, as it had been in several other places. It was part of a research programme aimed at developing therapeutic agents for Alzheimer's disease and eventually other brain dysfunctions. By April 1987 I had succeeded in convincing the company management that my team should use this probe and work on a diagnostic test for Alzheimer's disease. It was an ideal project. If the hypothesis proved to be correct and the amyloid beta protein gene was the Alzheimer's disease gene, then we would be in a position to develop a genetic test – a considerable step forward – within reasonable time and resource limits.

At the beginning of May 1987 I assigned the project to a post-doctoral fellow who had just arrived from England. We had the genetic probe but we still needed DNA samples. To that end we started collaborating with the Psychiatry Department of Stanford University, 2 miles away from the company. We did not have time to gather blood samples from extended families affected by Alzheimer's disease, so we opted to carry out association studies, in which we compared genetic-marker frequencies in DNA samples from two groups of unrelated individuals – a group of patients with documented Alzheimer's disease and a group of controls who had been certified free of the disease.

By early July we had discovered several genetic markers at the amyloid beta protein gene locus and we had completed the association studies. The results were disappointing: although there was some correlation between certain genetic markers and the diagnosis of Alzheimer's disease, it was too weak for a reliable diagnostic test. It also meant that the amyloid beta protein gene was not, as had been hoped, the gene responsible for Alzheimer's disease.

At the time I was in the lush countryside of Vermont, where I had been invited by David Housman, chairman of the Somatic Cell Genetics meeting, to give a paper on a different topic – genetic markers and heart disease. After learning about our results from my laboratory over the phone, I met Rudolph Tanzi, from James Gusella's laboratory, who was at the meeting to talk about their research on Alzheimer's disease. They had studied the occurrence of amyloid beta protein gene markers with Alzheimer's disease in affected families, and their data corroborated what we had established from our association studies: the amyloid beta protein gene could be ruled out as the main gene responsible for Alzheimer's disease. James Gusella's team was also able to show that the Alzheimer's disease locus is located about 8 million base pairs away from the amyloid beta protein gene – a very short chromosomic distance but a very long one for genetic-marker studies. So it goes with science! A more than likely hypothesis had been proved wrong by research.

James Gusella and his colleagues reported their findings in a September 1987 issue of *Nature*, where there was also another paper drawing similar conclusions as a result of collaboration between Belgian, German, Australian and London-based laboratories.

Since then researchers have concentrated their efforts on chromosome 21 in order to identify the mystery gene that causes at least one form of Alzheimer's disease. One hypothesis is that this gene codes for a protein exerting a major effect on the processing of the amyloid beta protein.

But this is by no means the end of the story. Indeed, other reports since have failed to confirm an association between chromosome 21 genetic markers and familial Alzheimer's disease in other affected families. In those cases, the disease could then be due to a genetic defect carried by other chromosomes.

Meanwhile, characterization of the complete gene demonstrated that the amyloid beta protein is only the severed portion of a much larger protein coded by a larger gene called amyloid precursor protein (APP). The current view is that the amyloid beta protein is an abnormal cleavage product of APP. But the real news came from the press before their publication in *Nature* on 21 February 1991. In this report, Alison Goates and her colleagues at St Mary's Hospital Medical School in London announced that a simple point-mutation within the APP gene does segregate with Alzheimer's disease in two families. Thus, a modified APP gene can actually be the cause of the disease in some instances! The DNA mutation creates a new BcLI restriction site and results in the making of a variant protein in which the 717th amino acid, a valine, is replaced with an isoleucine. Although, in these two families, it is transmitted with the disease to the offspring, the observed variation may in fact not necessarily be the causative factor. Much more data is warranted to answer that point and to determine the frequency of this form of the disease in the general population. Only then will we be able to decide whether the detection of this particular APP gene mutation constitutes a valid genetic test for a subset of Alzheimer's disease.

The observed discrepancies confirm our earliest suspicions that more than one gene is involved in the development of Alzheimer's disease and that the clinical disease entity is in fact heterogeneous, with more than one cause.

Identification of the defective genes and therefore of the molecular mechanisms resulting in the symptoms of Alzheimer's disease will permit us to come up with specific and efficient forms of treatment. Indeed, from a patient's point of view a diagnostic (or prognostic) test for dementia of the Alzheimer's type has no intrinsic value. It is useful only if a means of treatment or of preventing the illness is available. There is none at present, but other lines of research give us hope for a different form of therapy in the future.

Grafting Nerve Cells in the Brain

The main result of the neuropathological changes occurring in the brains of patients suffering from Alzheimer's disease is a progressive loss of a category of neurons – the cholinergic neurons. These particular nerve cells communicate with each other (transmit the nerve message) via the intermediary of a molecule they synthesize. This molecule, a neurotransmitter, is called acetylcholine. Found in both vertebrates and invertebrates, it is the most common neurotransmitter of the animal kingdom.

The current working hypothesis for an anti-Alzheimer's disease drug is to look for compounds that would supplement the acetylcholine deficit. It seems, however, that the same results could very well be achieved by a technique of gene therapy.

In the rat cholinergic neuron degeneracy can be avoided by perfusing the brain with a molecule naturally produced by the nerve cells called nerve growth factor (NGF). NGF plays a crucial role in the development of nerve cells in general. An interdisciplinary team of researchers from the Massachusetts General Hospital in Boston and from the Medical Center of the University of California in La Jolla had the idea of replacing the NGF perfusion process by grafting in rat brains some cells which could produce NGF in a continuous manner. The obvious candidates would be cholinergic neurons. Neurons, however, are very difficult to handle in laboratory settings. They cannot be cloned or manipulated at will. So the researchers used fibroblasts (skin and conjunctive tissue cells), which divide and grow easily in *in vitro* cultures. But fibroblasts do not produce NGF. To solve this problem, they attached the NGF gene to the genome of a retrovirus, which was then induced to infect the cultured fibroblasts. They could select and isolate the fibroblasts which had integrated the NGF gene in their DNA; these cells had become NGF-producing factories.

The next step was to graft some of these transformed fibroblasts into the rat brain regions where cholinergic neurons had been destroyed. The results were extremely encouraging: 92 per cent of the cholinergic neurons located downstream from the lesion were fully functional (instead of having degenerated following the lack of upstream stimulation resulting from the lesion) and, more interesting, had sent extensions towards the NGF-producing fibroblasts.

These results give serious hope for the development of a treatment to compensate for the loss of cholinergic neurons. These results are preliminary and, as the most common phrase in scientific research goes, 'further research is necessary'.

First of all, these experiments were performed on rats. They would need to be confirmed on humans, but not before we are absolutely sure that they present no danger. Second, fibroblasts may not be the ideal cells for this type of experiment. They were used only because of their convenience and availability; other cell types should be tested. And third, the *in vivo* experiment lasted only two weeks, thus ignoring any potential long-term effects. However, considering the pace of research in this area, we shall know within a few years whether or not this form of gene therapy is of serious value in the treatment of Alzheimer's disease.

Is Alzheimer's Disease an Automatic Concomitant of Ageing?

Probing into the complexity of Alzheimer's disease has prompted many questions about the more general phenomenon of ageing. Ageing is also a chronic, degenerative process advancing along an inexorable path. What is the actual difference between Alzheimer's disease and ageing? Isn't Alzheimer's disease simply a form of premature ageing? After all, deposition of senile plaques in the brain is a general observation. To a lesser degree, Alzheimer's disease-type lesions are present in the brains of older people, so that more than 80 per cent of humans reaching their tenth decade manifest the presence of marked senile plaques.

At the moment, there are two theories. The first claims that Alzheimer's disease is unavoidable. Whether at thirty-five, fifty, seventy or 150, everybody will be affected. The precise timing of its onset is a combination of genetic programming and environmental components. The second theory claims that ageing and Alzheimer's disease are caused by two different mechanisms. Although it is too early to say for sure, the first explanation seems more in line with what we know of the molecular mechanisms of chronic, degenerative illnesses: they generally result from an imbalance between physiological reactions so that symptoms gradually appear among patients before they do in 'normal' people. Once again, we need to wait for further research to give us the answers.

Schizophrenia, the Ultimate Form of Madness

AS WITH CARDIOVASCULAR DISEASE AND ALLERGIES, MENTAL ILLNESSES are another example of situations where individuals display a whole spectrum of symptoms, a whole array of behaviours. The line between normality and abnormality is set arbitrarily at a point between two extremes of a continuum according to subjective rules defined by the observer. For example, diagnosed by coronary angiography, heart disease is defined by some cardiologists as a disease representing 40 per cent obstruction of a major coronary artery; for others, this limit is 50 per cent, and more than one artery has to be affected by atherosclerosis. With mental illnesses, the cultural values of the observer also play a part. The boundaries in psychiatry are extremely fuzzy, and therefore difficult to define precisely. Many individuals are assigned to the nebulous zone of abnormality at one time or another. Some remain there all their lives, while others float in and out.

Loose Boundaries and Escaping Thoughts

Schizophrenia is a dramatic form of madness. It is actually the illness that fits the popular conception of madness most neatly. It usually starts in early adulthood, and thereafter affected individuals suffer episodes of varying severity for the rest of their lives. Therein lies the real drama. Although schizophrenics are abnormal (according to society's criteria) all their lives, their life expectancy is identical to that of the population at large.

To come up with a clinical definition of schizophrenia presents a major problem. The criteria used in Europe are somewhat different from those used in North America, based as they are on given sets of questions tailored to particular cultures. Both, however, are based on Western concepts, which would have little bearing outside the West's sphere of influence. Although a universal definition is impossible at this point because of both subjective evaluation and the complexity of the observed symptoms, it is possible to describe the symptoms which underlie the disorder.

First of all, schizophrenia is characterized by a group of psychotic symptoms: patients are subject to hallucinations and delusions, they hear voices, they experience thought disorders and have difficulty in concentrating on specific tasks. They imagine that their actions are controlled by alien powers, that people are able to read their thoughts or put thoughts in their minds. Victims of paranoid delusions, they believe themselves to be surrounded by hostile forces.

The behaviour of schizophrenic patients is erratic. They develop violent paranoid reactions towards people they are close to, and because of this, they become progressively alienated from family and friends, who are thus also affected by the emotional repercussions of the disease. Incapable of developing close relationships with anyone, they have a lower-than-normal reproductive rate.

Schizophrenics are often intelligent human beings with an elaborate sense of conceptualization, even if this sense may be distorted. Thus, although they can sometimes describe the appearance of hallucinatory phenomena, they feel powerless in trying to control their thoughts.

Schizophrenia: A Combination of Heredity and Environment

We do not know what triggers schizophrenia and why recurrent episodes of varying severity occur throughout the life. The underlying neurophysiological, biochemical and molecular mechanisms remain a complete mystery. It is clear, however, that two types of factor – environmental and genetic – participate interactively in the onset of the disease.

Several environmental factors have been put forward as possible causes for the onset of schizophrenia. These include emotional stress, adverse familial environment, mechanical blow on the head received at any time starting from the embryonic stage, and viral infection. Until proved irrelevant, these should be considered as serious working hypotheses. Our poor knowledge of environmental factors is only one source of frustration. The other concerns the genetic factors.

It has been clear for some time that genetic factors also play an important part in the onset of schizophrenia, for three main reasons. First, 1 per cent of any given population suffers from schizophrenia, no matter what country in the world we look at. Second, it has long been observed that several members of the same family are often affected by the disease. Other members, even if they do not exhibit the full spectrum of schizophrenia symptoms, are nevertheless subject to psychotic disorders; they display some of the milder features of schizophrenia and are subject to diverse forms of depression or to addiction to alcohol or drugs. And third, thanks to the study of twins we know that if one twin is schizophrenic, the other has an 80 per cent chance of being similarly afflicted.

Schizophrenia runs in families, but we do not know its mode of inheritance. If we had a precise understanding of its transmission, we could determine who is predisposed to the illness. There is a good reason why the mode of familial transmission has never been uncovered, a reason which had been suspected for some time: schizophrenia is a heterogeneous group of disorders. There are in fact several types of schizophrenia, and each type is caused by one or more genetic factors associated with one or more environmental factors. The clinical symptoms of schizophrenia are probably the manifestations of different diseases, each perhaps due to different molecular abnormalities.

In this respect, schizophrenia is conceptually identical to atherosclerosis or heart disease. The diagnostic term 'schizophrenia' refers to the clinical label of the observable, peripheral and subjectively defined symptoms of different diseases which may well be totally unrelated.

The Genetic Factors

Over the past few years these hypotheses have been accepted by modern psychiatrists and researchers in molecular neuropsychiatry. They were confirmed in November 1988 by two scientific articles in *Nature*. Not surprisingly, molecular genetics has come to the rescue of traditional psychiatry.

Definite proof of the existence of a hereditary component in schizophrenia was provided by Hugh Gurling's research team at the Department of Psychiatry, University of London. They have discovered genetic markers associated with the diagnosis of schizophrenia in seven unrelated families, five of whom live in Iceland and the other two in England. These markers function as signposts indicating the proximity of the schizophrenia gene. They are by no means the cause of this form of schizophrenia. However, we are now aware of the approximate location of the schizophrenia gene, for it can lie only within a short distance of the markers identified on this particular region of chromosome 5.

The gene located on chromosome 5, whose abnormality is responsible for schizophrenia, has not yet been identified, but it will be in the near future, because we know where to conduct further research. We also suspect that a variation of this single gene – whether it is a mutation, a deletion or a rearrangement – is responsible for the schizophrenia symptoms observed in the members of the seven families which participated in the investigation.

The schizophrenia puzzle, however, is far from being solved. Two major complications stand in the way – scientific investigation is never-ending and never clear-cut! The first complication arises from the conclusions drawn by Dr Gurling. The data show that the inheritance of the diseased schizophrenia gene – whatever this gene might be – is not sufficient to cause the inheritance of schizophrenia. Indeed, certain family members have inherited the gene but are not affected by the disease. The conclusion is that although one genetic factor has been uncovered, we need to admit the existence of other factors, both genetic and non-genetic. This is exactly what had been suspected for a long time.

The second complication was highlighted in an article in the same issue of *Nature* which reported the results of a separate study, conducted by Kenneth Kidd from Yale University and Luigi Cavalli-Sforza from Stanford University, on a Swedish family with eighty-one members, thirty-one of whom are affected by schizophrenia. This family had been intensively studied by several groups of researchers, whose conclusions were that the chromosome 5 genetic markers were not associated with the symptoms of schizophrenia. In this family, then, schizophrenia was caused by one or several genes located elsewhere in the genome, and not by a major gene situated on chromosome 5.

Thus the Icelandic and British patients suffer from a type of schizophrenia which is different from the one affecting the Swedes. This discrepancy suggests that what seems to be the same disease can result from at least two completely different molecular mechanisms. By the end of the summer of 1989 this conclusion was considerably strengthened by the work of at least four other laboratories: they too had found no association between chromosome 5 markers and symptoms of schizophrenia in several different patient families. This accumulation of evidence tells us that the type of schizophrenia caused by one or more defects of a major gene located on chromosome 5 is probably a fairly rare form.

Although these preliminary results are interesting and provocative, they are but a scratch on the surface of the schizophrenia blackbox. New avenues now await systematic exploration, and two specific questions immediately spring to mind: first, can we find out what the chromosome 5 abnormality consists of, and, second, what is the overall worldwide frequency of this form of schizophrenia? Both questions will be at least partially answered within the next few years.

The next step is to identify the gene whose abnormality is responsible for schizophrenia among the Icelandic and British patients studied by Hugh Gurling's team. Walking along chromosome 5 from the location of the genetic markers associated with schizophrenia to the gene itself will accomplish this task. These routine methods present no particular difficulty, and although they require a lot of work, they will lead to the characterization of this schizophrenia gene.

Genetic Testing of the Future

Specific DNA probes constructed on the basis of the known sequence of the gene will then allow the isolation of this as-yet-unknown gene from schizophrenic and non-schizophrenic patients. Comparison of the normal and abnormal gene sequences should define the precise abnormality, the DNA alteration, which causes schizophrenia. Identification of this DNA variation will have two immediate applications.

First, it will constitute an unmistakable diagnostic and, of course, prognostic test for detecting an individual's genetic predisposition towards this particular form of schizophrenia. It will not, however, be sufficient to predict exactly whether schizophrenia will manifest itself among individuals carrying this alteration. As mentioned earlier, several genetic and non-genetic factors interact together to trigger the disease. But we will have in our hands one of the main components involved in this form. Second, only at that stage will we be able to understand the resulting molecular and biochemical mechanisms causing the neurophysiological alterations making up this form of schizophrenia. And we will then finally be capable of conceptualizing and developing appropriate forms of treatment tailored to the causative molecular mechanisms.

Efficient Treatments Are Urgently Needed

Fortunately, psychiatrists have had access for quite a while to a battery of drugs which can stabilize the patient's state during the recurrent episodes of the disease. Butyrophenones such as haloperidol and phenothiazine drugs such as chlorpromazine offer symptomatic relief from the delusions and the hallucinations. Although they do not cure schizophrenia, they exert such beneficial effects that some patients who once had to be kept under surveillance in locked hospital wards can now lead an active life in mainstream society. These drugs, however, induce many unwanted side effects, such as restlessness, dystonia and continuous movements of head and tongue. So, even though the drugs represent a fundamental improvement in the care of schizophrenic patients, every physician would acknowledge the need for more effective and safer forms of treatment.

Although the schizophrenia gene located on chromosome 5 was not the unique factor triggering the illness among the Icelandic and British patients, it appears to be involved in the other mental ailments, such as milder psychoses, depressions, and drug and alcohol addictions, observed in the members from the affected families. The development of a treatment modality specifically adapted to this particular gene abnormality would thus find a broader field of application. It is probable that its effects, besides treating schizophrenia, would also extend to other psychoses and maybe to some types of depression and drug addiction.

Naturally, the ultimate cure for schizophrenia would consist of replacing the genes predisposing to the disorder by their healthy counterparts in affected individuals. Before reaching this stage, however, we need, first, to refine our methods of gene therapy and, second, to identify exactly which genes are responsible for the hereditary predisposition to schizophrenia.

What We Should Do in the Near Future

Before we engage in long-term and expensive programmes aimed at elaborating new kinds of drugs, we need to address the question of the frequency of the chromosome 5 schizophrenia gene abnormality. It appears today that researchers were lucky to detect this rare form in those particular families. Or is it a widespread illness? The answer to that question will affect the research policy and dictate the direction of any further investigation in this field. We do not know the answer at present, but several laboratories are well on the way to providing it. No technical obstacle stands in the way.

The DNA probes used by Hugh Gurling's team, as well as dozens of equivalent probes which can detect the same or similar genetic markers on this region of chromosome 5, are readily available worldwide. All that the scientists have to do now is to obtain access to populations of schizophrenic patients in order to determine the frequencies of these chromosome 5 markers. This is naturally easier said than done; the experimental steps involved still remain sophisticated. Once again, automation of these methodologies will greatly reduce the time and effort necessary to perform the research work.

A final word on this subject concerns the diagnosis of schizophrenia as a possible source of skewed frequencies. As in all other complex disorders, a major drawback is the uncertainty and subjective interpretation in the diagnosis of schizophrenia: first, because appropriate care, either by drug therapy or by psychiatric follow-up evaluation, is made more difficult and, second, because it is at this point impossible to define a homogeneous population of patients whose disease form is the result of identical molecular defects. What researchers study are heterogeneous groups comprised of individuals with various forms of schizophrenia.

We thus run into a dilemma. We have no current way of separating schizophrenia into its subgroups, which again underscores the need for a reliable diagnostic classification of the various forms of the disease, a gap that molecular genetics is soon expected to fill. However, to apply genetic-marker studies with maximum efficiency, we would need well-defined disease entities to look for differences in the DNA of the corresponding patients. Still, we have to start somewhere, and this is what several laboratories have already begun. Eventually, we will have a new and unambiguous classification of schizophrenia in which the different disease entities could be identifiable based on genetic markers.

_____

From Depression to Manic Excitation (As Molecular Genetics in Mental Illness)

BIPOLAR DISORDER IS THE FORM OF MAJOR AFFECTIVE DISORDER that we also call 'manic depression'. Here, the patient's mood classically alternates between two opposites: a manic state and a depressive state.

Symptoms of Depression and of Mania

We all experience feelings of depression from time to time and we all know what it means. It is a perfectly understandable mood which occurs as the result of distressing situations. We just learn to adjust and to cope with the consequences. Patients suffering from major depressive illness, however, live in a permanent, or extended, miserable state from which they are unable to escape by themselves. They cannot pinpoint any significant reason for this depression; their thoughts are slower and they cannot make decisions; they experience feelings of guilt, of unworthiness and of low self-esteem; they have difficulty in falling asleep and when they do, they wake up three or four hours later feeling even more tired. These patients feel they are drowning in a sea of despondency, lost in some kind of black hole that completely surrounds them and from which they do not have the strength to escape.

A manic phase is quite the opposite. It is characterized by hyperactivity, excessive cheerfulness and grandiose delusions. The patient is typically boisterous and displays embarrassing behaviour. He or she speaks rapidly, quickly shifting from one idea to another, jokes and teases other people while paying little attention to the environment. In this state the person can imperil his or her social life by gambling and running up very high debts, and by becoming excessively violent if feeling he or she has been crossed or provoked.

The term 'bipolar disorder' has gained acceptance over 'manic depression' because patients can alternate between depressive and manic states (that would fit the meaning of 'manic depression'), manic and relatively 'normal' phases, and 'normal' and depressive moods to varying degrees between these extremes. Bipolar disorders can be controlled with lithium salts, but patients need to be hospitalized at the beginning of the treatment.

Criteria for diagnoses of major affective disorders such as bipolar disorder are purely subjective: no biological marker has been identified. Although this is not proof of a genetic basis, bipolar disorder (like depression) is known to run in families. Several research teams have unsuccessfully tried to determine precisely its mode of transmission. Of course, the part played by the environment is also very important. Here again, it is clear that certain individuals display an increased genetic susceptibility to the disease, which manifests itself under certain conditions determined by environmental surroundings.

Genetic Markers and Manic Depression

The field of molecular genetics has provided the tools necessary to obtain clues about the genetic component of the disease. Janice A. Egeland of the University of Miami School of Medicine in Florida and David Housman of the Massachusetts Institute of Technology in Boston took the challenge and looked for genetic markers associated with the clinical manifestations of bipolar disorder. In order to perform linkage analysis studies, the researchers needed extended affected families with well-documented clinical diagnoses of major affective disorder.

They went to southern Pennsylvania and studied a genetically and culturally isolated Amish population. The Amish are a religious community with a natural, healthy life style: they follow a strict diet, do not smoke, do not drink alcohol, do not use drugs and effectively ignore the twentieth century. In other words, there are no factors such as alcohol or drugs whose temporary effects can mimic those of affective disorders.

The teams of Janice Egeland and David Housman investigated three generations of three Amish families. Out of a total of eighty-one individuals, fourteen were affected by some form of bipolar disorder and five had severe depression. In February 1987 they reported in *Nature* the association between genetic markers located on the tip of chromosome 11 and predisposition to bipolar disorder, as well as possibly to major depression. They concluded that this chromosome

11 gene effect is dominant: that is, Amish individuals who inherit it will suffer from bipolar disorder. They cautioned, however, that this gene defect probably does not underlie all cases of bipolar disorders. This prudent statement was in fact confirmed by two other reports in the same issue of *Nature*. One described the results of a study carried out on Icelandic families and the other on non-Amish American families; both failed to demonstrate association between chromosome 11 genetic markers and bipolar disorder in the respective populations.

Miron Baron of Columbia University College of Physicians and Surgeons and the New York State Psychiatric Institute then published the results of an investigation on a number of Israeli families. He showed the presence of a gene for major depression at the end of the long arm of chromosome X, near the gene responsible for colour blindness. Another investigation placed such a gene at the other end of chromosome X, while the team of Elliot Gershon of the National Institute of Mental Health in Bethesda, Maryland, demonstrated the absence of linkage between major depression and chromosome X in the families that they investigated. Quite a mixture of conflicting data! What can we make out of them?

Disillusionment of Molecular Geneticists

The exploration of genetic components underlying mental illnesses has had similar results to studies of cardiovascular disease, and there has been disillusionment in this field as well. Research has failed to meet the high expectations raised five or six years ago. Many scientists have been discouraged and some have even started to question the real validity of these investigations. However, we just need to put the data that has been generated in perspective. Careful analysis of the discrepancies in published results reveals that they are in fact sources of hope rather than of discouragement.

Among neuropsychiatric disorders the success story remains Huntington's disease. The symptoms of this disease typically appear in patients who are in their thirties. They consist of uncontrollable muscle movements in the face, accompanied by progressive dementia. Although movements can be controlled by drugs such as tetrabenazine, the mental deterioration is untreatable. Huntington's disease is a genetic disease whose mode of transmission had been clearly established as autosomal dominant (one gene defect located on a non-sexual chromosome): a person who inherits the affected gene suffers from the disease before the age of forty. This still leaves time for reproduction, which explains why this devastating illness has not been destroyed by evolution. The teams of James Gusella of Harvard University Medical Center and Nancy Wexler of the University of Michigan Medical Center, Ann Arbor, discovered back in 1983 that the gene responsible for Huntington's disease was located on chromosome 4. That was a major step forward in the race to decipher the genetic components of neuropsychiatric illnesses. Eight years later, however, scientists are still trying to walk along chromosome 4 in order to identify the unknown gene whose abnormality causes the disease.

Chromosome 4 genetic markers have allowed the development of a diagnostic (and prognostic) test for the disease, but so far have failed to provide clues to the molecular mechanism involved. In other words, the contribution of molecular genetics to the management of Huntington's disease has stopped at the stage of genetic counselling. It has not yet provided efficient therapeutic measures, let alone a cure.

In the case of such mental disorders as Alzheimer's disease, schizophrenia, bipolar disorder and major depressive disorder, however, we have not even reached that stage. The main difficulty here is that we are after genes that may predispose an individual to the disorders rather than causing them. From this apparently trivial difference stem all the complications we are now facing. Hence the conflicting results reported by several groups of researchers on all of these mental disorders.

Problems to Overcome and Reasonable Hopes

The causes of discrepancies in results generated by molecular geneticists in the study of mental illness are similar to those applying to the study of atherosclerosis and cardiovascular disease. There are five major reasons: genetic heterogeneity; misdiagnosis of affected relatives; lack of availability of large affected families; imperfect genetic linkage maps; and inappropriate statistical methodologies.

Alzheimer's disease, schizophrenia and bipolar disorders are all heterogeneous disorders. Multiple causes and probably various molecular defects interact with environmental factors to produce similar clinical entities. The ultimate proof of genetic heterogeneity will be to identify all disease-causing genes and to unravel all the corresponding molecular mechanisms. This will take time: maybe years for Alzheimer's disease and probably decades for schizophrenia and major affective disorders.

A major problem is to perform a correct diagnosis of all affected members of families under study — a tremendously difficult task.

Criteria of disease definition vary between laboratories and are constantly modified. They are based on the subjective interpretation of the psychiatrist making the assessment. What we lack are biological markers, clinically identifiable values that can be quantified. Abnormal levels of numerous chemical components in the blood or in the cerebrospinal fluid have been reported over the years. None of these is satisfactory or can be used to make a reliable diagnosis. Furthermore, affected family members may not show symptoms of the disease at the time of the evaluation. Indeed, these diseases display both variable penetrance and variable expressivity. So, making a global judgement on the severity of the disease is very difficult, because its manifestations change over time. The case of schizophrenia is particularly representative. Some members of the families of schizophrenic patients display milder forms of the disease or only some of its symptoms. We then speak of 'schizoid' features, of which a whole spectrum exists. We should not be fooled by the large number of technical terms attempting to provide some kind of definition. Vague terminology is always a sure sign of uncertainty and ignorance.

The irony is that although the aim of molecular genetics is to provide a new and precise classification of the different causes of mental illnesses, in the best of all cases we would need such a classification to perform these studies efficiently. This situation slows down the rate at which data can be generated.

We are looking for genes that predispose an individual to particular illnesses. The effect of these abnormal genes is dampened by phenomena such as low penetrance. To detect them therefore requires an increase in the power of the analysis, and that means increasing the sample size. In other words, we need to have access to many clinically well-characterized, large multigeneration families. This is what is lacking at the moment.

If we take the chromosome 5 genetic markers associated with schizophrenia, it is clear by now that what has been examined is only a small subset of the disease. It has recently been suggested that a confirmation of the reported association may require as many as 200 additional families of schizophrenic patients. Several laboratories and international organizations are actively working to collect DNA samples from as many well-characterized families as possible.

What makes linkage studies possible is the availability of genetic markers. As mentioned previously, we have identified thousands of RFLPs of all kinds and are finding new ones every day. Although discovery of RFLPs all along the DNA molecule has permitted us to generate preliminary maps of the human genome, markers are still spaced unevenly; some are too far apart and several regions are still effectively large gaps. Finding additional high-quality markers – the aim of the genome projects – will increase the likelihood of detecting disease-causing genes.

Last but not least in the list of drawbacks is the inappropriateness of our current statistical methodologies. Association between genetic markers and clinical symptoms in families is called linkage analysis. In order to perform linkage analysis, we need to specify the mode of transmission of the disease under study. Since in most cases this is simply unknown, we have to make educated guesses and test several hypotheses. The same holds true for the number of genes involved, as well as for the penetrance value. Of course, we have to be aware that we are bound to make some errors at each one of these steps. The real worry is that these errors make it easier to reject than to detect associations between markers and disease.

We have been so used to the concept of 'one gene–one disease' that most computer programs handle only the transmission of one gene at a time in multigeneration families. Yet we know now that most neuropsychiatric disorders are characterized by a multifactorial, polygenic mode of inheritance. The advent of super-computers will make it easier to develop programs that will be able to analyse the simultaneous inheritance of several genetic locations.

In conclusion, the results generated by genetic-marker studies have triggered an interest in neuropsychiatric illnesses. Scientists have already identified the chromosomal location of the genetic alterations responsible, for example, for the monogenic Huntington's disease. In the case of multifactorial illnesses, they have already found the location of several genes conferring genetic susceptibility to Alzheimer's disease, bipolar disorder, major depressive disorder and schizophrenia. The failure of other research teams to reproduce these data does not refute their validity, which needs to be confirmed before moving along any further. And in any case, reasonable explanations for the conflicting data have been put forward; they should be evaluated as quickly as possible.

We are living in exciting times and have no reason to feel discouraged. The disillusionment felt by certain people, some of them scientists, is due to the fact that molecular genetics has not performed miracles. Well, it never set out to do so. What is a certainty at this point is the extraordinary amount of work lying ahead. Resolving the puzzle of mental illnesses will require a major effort, but we have the tools to perform this task. Preliminary but encouraging results have shown us that we are on the right track.

PART THREE _____

Nature, Culture and Genetics – a Matter of Opinion

Increasing Life Expectancy: At What Price?

THE PROGRESS MADE OVER THE PAST FEW YEARS WITH THE ADVENT of the methods of molecular biology has opened new horizons. Biomedical researchers have been given new tools with which to intensify the battle against disease. What will be the consequences for the individual on a day-to-day basis?

The Fight Against Monogenic Diseases

Genetic-marker studies have allowed the development of prognostic tests for several hereditary diseases with a monogenic mode of transmission, including sickle cell anaemia, various forms of thalassaemia, cystic fibrosis, Huntington's disease, haemophilia, phenylketonurea and Duchenne's myopathy. Researchers are now moving towards DNA identification of (and therefore the development of diagnostic tests for) the 3,500 or so reported genetic diseases.

The expression of a monogenic disease is a clear-cut process: an individual carrying in his or her genome the disease-causing DNA abnormality is, or will be, affected by the disease. Such diseases cause long periods of ill-health and require expensive, time-consuming and often painful treatment. The most serious ones are incompatible with life and lead to stillbirth; others result in early death. They always have social and familial implications. Parents who have had one sick child live in the fear of giving birth to another.

DNA tests allow accurate prenatal diagnosis of diseases severe enough to warrant referral for pregnancy termination. A prenatal DNA test gives a definite answer. If the foetus is not affected, the pregnancy can go on. A positive diagnosis leaves the parents with a choice: whether to terminate the pregnancy. At present amniocentesis is the most widely used method to obtain a DNA sample of the foetus. This procedure is performed in the sixteenth week of pregnancy, which means that if necessary a termination can take place between the seventeenth and twentieth weeks. As chorionic biopsy becomes safer and more readily available, diagnosis will be possible between the seventh and tenth weeks of pregnancy, considerably reducing the trauma of termination.

DNA testing is very sophisticated and is carried out by only a few reference laboratories. Although it is still considered a luxury, its use is rapidly spreading. The cost is high compared to other medical tests, but improvement in technology and the automation of the experimental procedures will certainly bring it down in time. Actually, concerns about cost–benefit ratios have been raised again and again. Will the savings made from the benefits of DNA testing services outweigh the cost of implementing and running the reference laboratories? Several cost–benefit analyses have revealed that already DNA screening laboratories are associated with impressive savings, so DNA testing should be encouraged and quickly implemented within hospital settings.

New developments will make it even more cost-effective. Indeed, the number of diagnostic tests using genetic markers rises almost every month. Most of the expense comes from the administrative structure necessary to admit the patients, draw their blood and send the samples to reference laboratories, where they can be processed for DNA isolation. Once the patient's DNA is available, a whole battery of tests can be run as easily as a single test and the cost becomes minimal.

Detection of Genetic Predisposition: The Ultimate Weapon for Prevention

In the case of multifactorial disorders, the value of DNA technology lies in the development of genetic tests that can drastically improve the early detection of an individual's susceptibility to a disease. It will allow the identification of high-risk individuals to whom appropriate preventive intervention can be tailored.

The need for accurate susceptibility testing has become evident over the past few years. The actual emphasis of preventive medicine is based on the large-scale implementation of routine medical check-ups. They are the ideal way to confirm that a person is in perfect health. However, a report from a group of American doctors has shown that the predictive value of routine examinations for some forms of cardiovascular disease and cancer, among several other afflictions, is negligible. The cost-effectiveness of medical examinations would be drastically improved by concentrating on the known weak points of a person, and this is precisely what genetic testing proposes to do.

This observation is in line with the current preoccupation of modern medicine, whose goal is to gradually switch from a therapeutic to a preventive approach. The basis for conventional, therapeutic medicine is to treat the symptoms of a disease. With this traditional approach, doctors can hope only to offer palliatives for the peripheral manifestations of illnesses. They are not able to get to the roots of a disease but can only aim at ameliorating its symptoms. Sometimes it is possible to fight the cause of an illness – this is what happens, for example, when antibiotics are used to wipe out a bacterial infection – but in most other cases there is no equivalent to antibiotic treatments.

Preventive medicine, on the other hand, involves predicting what disease (or diseases) a person is susceptible to well before the first symptoms appear. In parallel with the development of predictive tests, medical researchers are also working on the elaboration of precise and efficient measures that can be applied to prevent the onset of the disease. The widespread use of cholesterol-lowering medications to stop the progression of heart disease among high-risk patients constitutes a particularly good example of preventive medicine.

Prevention has become a key concept today, not confined to the medical field alone; crime prevention and the prevention of road accidents are two other much-debated examples. Of course, we can attempt to prevent only what we already know and can predict. That means knowing all the variables of the event we want to avoid. Medical researchers are certainly not yet in that position, but it is the goal they are aiming for.

Scientists can develop prognostic tests for all disorders with some hereditary component. Although this may sound like science fiction, predictive testing for cardiovascular disease, all types of cancer, osteoporosis and mental illnesses will one day be part of the battery of routine medical check-ups. It will then be possible to determine from early childhood who is likely to suffer one day from a heart attack. How will the individual react to the results of such a test? What will be the consequences of preventive medicine on society's attitude and life style?

The Story of Mr Smith

Let us imagine for an instant the story of someone we will call Mr Smith. Mr Smith has to have a medical check-up so that he can apply for life insurance. He is thirty-five years old, considers himself in good health and leads a peaceful life with his family, friends and colleagues at work. The results of the tests, however, indicate that Mr Smith is likely to suffer one day from a myocardial infarct. Nothing is really alarming at present, but several signs confirm this conclusion. Both his serum cholesterol level and his arterial blood pressure are somehow elevated. He smokes half a packet of cigarettes a day and he drinks fairly regularly – maybe a little bit too much on occasions. Not only does he have a sedentary job, but he also has neither the time nor the will to exercise regularly. Finally, and this may be the most serious sign, his father died of a heart attack before the age of sixty.

Taken individually, each of these signs indicates a weak risk factor for cardiovascular disease. Taken together, they drastically increase the overall risk. The family doctor will without any doubt tell Mr Smith to take immediate measures: he or she will ask him to start eating a healthier diet, to take regular exercise and to stop smoking. Furthermore, in certain special cases Mr Smith might be given medication to reduce both the high serum cholesterol levels and the hypertension.

All these measures prescribed by the doctor are thought to be helpful in the prevention of heart disease. To Mr Smith, they mean that he has to modify his life style, and what is more, he will have to maintain these drastic modifications for his whole life. Yet for him this shift in his way of life is being imposed by an abstract concept: a probability that he will suffer one day (in a distant future) from a heart attack. Unless exceptional circumstances accelerate the progression of the disease, he will be fine for at least another twenty years. Not to mention that there is always a chance that he will escape the risk of heart disease, even if he does not change any of his dietary and behavioural patterns. Mr Smith does not feel directly concerned, because a putative heart attack is not a concrete event. It has never happened to him personally, so he does not know what it really means.

We all know the conclusion. Mr Smith is not going to modify his life style, or if he does, it will be in an episodic manner and for a short period of time. The only event to force the Mr Smiths of this world to change their mind and embark on a 'healthier' way of life is the first heart attack which they are lucky enough to survive.

We Can Prevent Disease

The availability of predictive tests for an individual's susceptibility to heart disease will represent a major milestone in the fight against this devastating illness. Identifying individuals who are at higher risk because of their genetic susceptibility would seem to be a good start. But then what? What can we do about it? Are there satisfactory, preventive measures for someone whose results are positive? The answer is yes. A person at higher risk for heart disease can switch to low-cholesterol food, keep his or her weight down, exercise moderately, refrain from smoking and control his or her blood pressure. Furthermore, several drugs are available to decrease serum cholesterol levels and arterial blood pressure. In short, we do have a wide array of means to reduce the risk of cardiovascular disease. Although these means are particularly effective for individuals who have a higher risk because of their genetic constitution, they also benefit the rest of the population. Furthermore, molecular biology will add its own contribution to these measures, in the form of even more appropriate and more efficient recombinant DNA drugs.

Although it is most certainly against heart disease that scientists have discovered the greatest number of preventive measures, other illnesses can also be contained. Anti-oxidant agents, which are found in green vegetables, for example, are useful against cancers, as are vitamins, because of their protective action against dietary and environmental toxins. Oestrogen therapy, as well as other hormones (such as parathyroid hormone and calcitonin), and fluoride compounds are efficient ways of preventing osteoporosis; they certainly seem more appropriate than the ingestion of massive doses of calcium. Prevention of mental disorders is still an open field, but considerable progress is expected within the next few years.

Do We Want to Change Our Life Style?

We already have ways of preventing many illnesses, such as heart disease, and current medical practice is to take advantage of them. The real question, though, is this: would we change our life style if we knew that we were at higher risk of developing a debilitating or lethal illness? It seems at first sight that the answer is no. The anecdote about Mr Smith will ring a bell in most people's minds, and it seems as if his attitude is supported by several epidemiological studies carried out over long periods of time.

A large-scale investigation conducted in America over a period of ten years and costing $115 million, the MRFIT (Multiple Risk Factor Intervention Test) studied 13,000 participants predisposed to cardiac disease. Their aim was initially to determine whether the reduction of risk factors would also lower the mortality rate of these individuals. The participants were all volunteers and very motivated to follow the advice given to them. After having been informed of their respective risks, they were separated into two groups of equal size. Those who belonged to the first group returned to the care of their family doctors, while those from the second group were closely monitored in specialized institutions and by qualified personnel who helped them to change their life styles as much as was possible.

This study confirmed results obtained by similar projects: the reduction of certain risk factors lowered the rate of heart disease. However, it came up with another unexpected conclusion: subjects from the second group, closely followed and constantly encouraged and guided by trained professionals, had no more modified their life style than those from the first group. The medical researchers who designed the programme learned a lesson: warning a person that he or she runs an increased risk of developing a disease is not a sufficient signal for this person to change his or her life style.

Scientists involved with programmes such as the MRFIT have often displayed a pessimistic and somewhat defeatist attitude. Moreover, they have also been accused of having an élitist view of medical prevention: why seek to force people to change their habits on the grounds of a simple probability of a 'higher-than-normal' risk? Even if the disease is certain to occur, does anyone have the right to tell an individual what to do?

At the moment, the root of the problem is that the available tools are inadequate. No current test can predict accurately who will suffer from a myocardial infarction. The situation will be different once the reliable prognostic tests that DNA technology can provide are available. Certainty will then replace probability and we will have more cards in our hands to make the appropriate decisions affecting our future.

When we are asked to modify our life style because of susceptibility to a certain disease, we find it very difficult. Breaking away from our habits is hard to do. What is the solution, then? Are we going to keep on spending time and money on useless investigations, useless, because the individuals concerned will not take note of the results? Not at all. These investigations are necessary to identify both the risks associated with illnesses and the measures available to fight them, but it is impossible to look for an answer because the questions themselves have not yet been asked correctly. In the future, people will change their life style in the right direction, not because as individuals we will suddenly become more responsive but because the whole of society will change its life style.

Modify Your Life Style: A Fashionable Undertaking

How will this change take place? First of all, we know that people can modify their customs and values. It is not easy, because habits represent deeply rooted manifestations of a person's cultural heritage and, as such, constitute a very emotional issue. Changing this heritage, or part of it, can be achieved and accepted by a person only as the result of a conscious decision on his or her part. Decisions by other people – doctors, researchers or whoever – will not have any lasting impact.

All changes are feasible. After all, society is a dynamic entity which must adapt to the needs it creates for itself, and this cultural evolution moulds new customs. Several isolated programmes have demonstrated that food habits can change. Take North Karelia, for example, a small Finnish town where the rate of cardiac disease was among the highest in the world. There were two main culprits. First, the consumption of butter, eggs and other foods which should be eaten with moderation was gargantuan. Second, DNA from the Finns bears a particular mutation which leads to the modification of a protein participating in cholesterol transport and clearance, apolipoprotein E (apoE). The modified apoE, frequently encountered in Finland, is less efficient in fulfilling its role as a cholesterol clearer. Blood levels of cholesterol, as well as other lipids, increase and contribute to the mechanism by which they are deposited on arterial walls and thicken atheromatous plaques, up to the point of a heart attack.

Supported by the Finnish government, a group of researchers started a campaign to change the dietary habits of North Karelian citizens. Through massive advertising, by disseminating information in schools and in factories, by making sure that shops were supplied with low-cholesterol food, they succeeded in modifying the diet of the inhabitants.

Programmes such as these, however, represent pilot projects carried out on volunteers under the supervision of researchers. Even in these controlled conditions, they do not always work: medical organizations failed to start a similar campaign that had been planned in another Finnish town. How about the rest of the population? How about other countries? It takes more than a restricted, pilot project to trigger a long-term change in eating habits. Surely it has to be something drastic? Well, yes and no.

Naturally, the change is drastic, but it has already taken place and is rapidly spreading through a powerful channel: fashion.

A few years back it suddenly became fashionable to be diet-conscious. Today, concerns about food are part of the new code of modern living. Anti-cholesterol and other 'prudent' dietary campaigns have exerted a profound influence on our attitudes to food – probably more than we realize. Statistics show that in less than ten years we have generally cut down on sugar, salt, cholesterol and other fatty substances. Polyunsaturated and low-fat margarines are gaining in popularity. We eat fewer fried foods, more fish, more fruit and vegetables, more fibre and more wholemeal bread. We drink more skimmed milk. These are but a few examples from a very long list.

Industrialized countries have reached a point of wealth where they can afford to be discriminating in their food choices and adopt a balanced diet in the interests of good health. Consumer associations have raised awareness of food quality. People have become resistant to the idea of food additives, such as artificial colourings and flavourings, and they have become used to questioning the practices of the food industry.

Although we are making progress, our diets are still far from being compatible with perfect health. We are learning by trial and error. Nutrition experts agree that we eat too little iron and drink too much alcohol; we may have gone overboard with our concern about cholesterol; we do not need to take excessive amounts of extra vitamins (as happens often in America); we should eat more fruit and vegetables. In conclusion, it is true to say that we can eat a little bit of everything – not too much, not too little.

Moreover, if we take a close look at ideal regimens, we quickly realize that we have every reason to be careful in eating foods considered as healthy, and that massive amounts of these can damage our health. Smoked meats are rich in nitrosamines (bad for the liver); grilled meats contain chemical compounds resulting from pyrolysis of fats and protein (bad for stomach and intestines); fish is loaded with heavy metals such as lead, mercury and cadmium (bad for kidneys and prostate); peanuts and certain breakfast cereals that have been stored in humid surroundings contain aflatoxins liberated by certain types of mould (extremely carcinogenic for the liver); fruit and vegetables have vitamins, mineral salts and fibres and thereby protect against certain types of cancer, but they also contain liver-damaging nitrates. The key word is moderation, as in so many aspects of life.

Modern society is interested in more than just a healthy diet. No smoking, weight loss and maintenance of regular physical activity are measures which have been taken on board and given affirmation by television commercials and magazine advertisements.

We are living in exciting times in many respects. We have entered a period of fundamental change, with cultural evolution progressing by quick steps. Two approaches, once contradictory, have finally met: what the individual must do, as dictated by medical advice, and what the individual wishes to do. Feeling good and healthy, paying a lot of attention to one's physical appearance, increasing one's leisure time while practising some sport – these are practical recommendations advocated by the medical community. They are also what society demands. This demand stems from a conscious decision to adopt a different way of life. The result is that a person who decides to live a healthier life is no longer perceived as a 'freak', while those who disagree with the emergence of new diets still have the freedom to decide their own regimen.

We Live Longer

The combination of detection and prevention is a powerful one, and it is contributing to increased life expectancy. The terms 'life expectancy' and 'life span' are often used interchangeably, but they have different meanings. Life expectancy is the average number of years of life expected in a population by an individual at birth. Life span is the maximum age that can be reached by an individual of a given species. In humans life span is a much-debated subject: we do not have birth records for those people who have claimed to be 130 or over; however, cases of 115-year-old individuals are known. It seems that life span has remained unchanged for quite a while, but life expectancy is a different matter. In the Western world it was about forty by 1880, and forty-five in 1900 and in 1983 it was seventy-one for men and seventy-eight for women.

The victory over infectious diseases has almost doubled humans' life expectancy over the past century. The battle against more chronic types of disease now strengthens the trend towards extending it even further. Is life expectancy going to increase indefinitely or are there any limits? There are two different strands of thought among experts on the subject of ageing. The first is based on *in vitro* experiments. Cells grown in laboratory conditions undergo a predictable and finite number of divisions, and then stop replicating. Using such observations, some investigators have postulated that human life expectancy is rapidly approaching a barrier at about eighty-five years.

This claim, however, has been challenged by scientists holding a different opinion: they see no reason why life expectancy should not be much higher than eighty-five. It is true that most organs of the human body show functional decline upon ageing; however, it seems that none of them presents sufficient impairment for death to result in the absence of disease, even at a very old age. Autopsies on people over ninety who died of 'natural' causes often reveal that these people have in fact succumbed to undetected infections. Several models predict that the life expectancy for white women will be ninety years by 2080. This figure is probably underestimated because it does not take into account the rapid decrease in the mortality rate that has been consistently observed among elderly people.

The situation in the future will be that the death rate remains low until a certain age and that the great majority of deaths will then occur over a very short period. With the assumption that the onset of chronic diseases will be delayed by the implementation of massive prevention campaigns, diseases that a person is susceptible to will strike in the later years of life (this phenomenon is referred to as the 'compression of morbidity').

The direct consequences of this situation are that the number of older people will grow rapidly and there will be a greater need for extensive medical care in the later years of life. If, in parallel, we take into account a decreasing birth rate, the imbalance between the working part of the population and the part composed of retired individuals will be accentuated. Resources allocated to social security and, in particular, to the health care of the elderly are already stretched to such an extent that they have become major political issues. Many observers have expressed concern about a potentially explosive situation in the future.

The problem will be exacerbated in countries such as the People's Republic of China, where families are normally only allowed one child in an effort to contain the explosive birth rate. What will happen in fifty years, when half the population has passed retirement age?

The Marriage of Nature with Nurture

WHAT I DISLIKE MOST ABOUT THE PHRASE 'NATURE VS NURTURE' IS THE way it polarizes the two concepts, placing them in stark opposition to each other, as arch-enemies doomed to clash until the end of time, or until one has finally triumphed over the other. This problem is more than a mere trick of language. It reflects the stark distinction between two irreconcilable trends of scientific thought.

On one side, proponents of 'Nature' adopt a totally deterministic view of the world's evolution, and in particular the evolution of living species. They believe that the manifestations of life on earth, including multiple aspects such as behaviour and disease, follow predetermined pathways programmed by the genetic blueprint. On the other side, supporters of the concept encompassed by the single word 'Nurture' are convinced that all attributes and properties of living beings result exclusively from the effects of environmental conditions.

Fooled by such inflexible lines of reasoning, diehard anthropologists defending 'Nurture' and intransigent and uncompromising biologists rooting for 'Nature' have frequently engaged in endless and bitter battles. Despite what we know today, these feuds aimed at proving which of the two heritages (genetic or cultural) constitute life's driving force are still conducted by many people, including scientists respected in their specialist fields. They inevitably reach deadlock because there can be no winner and no loser – that much we have learned. Both sides are partly right, and the positions they take are not antagonistic but complementary. To the best of our knowledge, life's processes occur as a result of phenomena which are combinations of genetic and environmental forces.

Three Blind Men and an Elephant

The parable of the blind men and the elephant sums up this situation well. One day three blind men who were travelling met with an elephant. None of them had ever heard of the existence of such an animal, and they each tried to give their own description of it. Since they could not see it, they had to get close to it and touch it, trying to find analogies with what they had encountered before.

'An elephant is like the trunk of a tree,' declared the first blind man, who had touched the elephant's leg.

'Not at all. It is like the branch of a willow,' replied the second one, who had touched the tail.

'You are wrong,' said the third one firmly, after patting the elephant's belly. 'It is like a giant barrel.'

Of course, they were all right and described to the best of their ability what they had experienced. Obtaining a full picture of the elephant would require taking into consideration the reports of the three men, but also exchanges of ideas, comparisons of results and additional investigations.

This is the stage that we have reached today in our evaluation of 'Nature *vs* Nurture'. Quantum jumps in our understanding of what behaviour really is necessitate the integration of results from investigators working in all concerned fields of study. Repeated opposition is nevertheless understandable, because it reflects our lack of complete knowledge of the truth. The compulsion to frame acquired knowledge into convenient simplifications finds its root in a mental reaction against the complexity of observable phenomena pertaining to life.

Heart attacks, cancer, intelligence, ageing, alcohol addiction or uncontrollable urges to gamble, to name but a few concerns of everyday life, represent very complicated puzzles, difficult to assess and to decipher. In any case, both genetic and environmental factors play a role in their appearance and progression. Overall global manifestations of disease and behaviour are the consequence of complementary and cooperative effects among these factors. The major challenge for medical and scientific research is to identify not only all of these factors but also the respective parts played by each of them, as well as the global effects of their complex and intricate interactions.

Abnormality Explains the Norm

Diseases constitute excellent model systems to help us identify and comprehend the myriad reactions taking place constantly in a living organism. Indeed, effects and symptoms expressed in the form of clinical manifestations represent deviations from normality. In an individual suffering from a particular disease, values measured by the physician or the clinical laboratory (be they blood pressure or serum cholesterol levels, activity of a particular enzyme, blood calcium or magnesium rates, or height and weight measurements) appear to be different from the normal physiological range of values defined in tables constructed after the recording of observations carried out in thousands of individuals. Abnormal values represent the indicators of drastic alterations occurring in specific biochemical reactions of the organism, and they make it easier to test the implicated mechanisms.

It is somehow conceptually difficult to characterize a normal biochemical mechanism or physiological pathway in an organism that hosts billions of simultaneous reactions. The characterization is facilitated by the investigation of an obvious abnormality in an affected person when compared with an unaffected sample of individuals. This is why the unravelling of the molecular principles underlying human disease is a prerequisite to understanding how and why we exist and function.

The value of this approach in our battle against the unknown can be demonstrated by asking the following question: how would you go about establishing a regional map of the different functions of the brain? This would be impossible if you simply decided to look at an isolated brain and tried to figure out what all the different parts do. You would need to design a carefully planned set of experiments to answer the question. The obvious approach is to destroy selectively one part after the other and observe and record the effects of the localized lesion: the destruction of one particular zone will, for example, induce loss of speech, or breathing impairment or blindness.

The problem with such a research programme is one of ethics: who would you choose as subjects for experimentation? Even if a scientist was sadistic enough to come up with such a project, chances of recruiting volunteers would be virtually nil, whatever the financial compensation offered (needless to say, brain damage is irreversible). Besides, a grant application calling for the funding of this project would not even reach the ethical committee.

Yet a similar conceptual strategy has been followed, with, however, a notable difference. Physicians and scientists have carefully registered information from subjects whose brains were damaged as a consequence of accidents or of war wounds. Painstaking research has enabled them to correlate localized brain lesions with corresponding impaired functions, and this is how the first maps delineating the roles of the different brain regions have been drawn.

Experimental procedures of increasing sophistication have contributed to a gradual refinement of our general knowledge. Today molecular neurobiology asks the questions directly to isolated nerve cells or to their expressed genetic material, and thereby by-passes the need to carry out scientific investigations on human beings. Answers spring right out of the test tube!

The Easy Stuff

With the study of the so-called multifactorial diseases, or of the many aspects of human behaviour, we have come a long way from simple situations summarized as 'one cause—one effect', such as infectious diseases and monogenic disorders.

Infection represents one type of such a process that is easy to conceptualize: one infectious agent causes one infectious disease. A bacterium called Koch's bacillus causes tuberculosis; a virus labelled HIV is the agent responsible for AIDS.

Unifactorial, monogenic diseases provide another example. An abnormality found in one affected gene is the cause of one genetic disease. A single deleterious mutation in the human beta-globin gene causes sickle cell anaemia; various mutations in the dystrophin gene lead to the development of Duchenne's muscular dystrophy; DNA variations at the location of the gene encoding the protein called factor VIII coagulation factor are responsible for haemophilia. Of the 3,500 or so reported genetic diseases, the list of those which can be identified with their corresponding DNA abnormalities becomes longer almost every week.

More Complicated Even Than Its Name

Multifactorial. This complicated adjective applies to the most common human diseases, as well as to all aspects of human behaviour. Meanwhile, we know that truth generally lies in simplicity. Does this mean, then, that we are far from the truth?

In a society geared towards specialization, people can seek refuge in their own personal ivory tower, confining themselves to the roles they have been assigned. The fragmentation of the various disciplines is greatly facilitated by the use of exclusive vocabulary. A legal document, for example, seems to be unnecessarily difficult for the lay person to follow; a garage mechanic will tend to make the simplest job sound difficult, and so on.

Science and medicine have their own collection of interesting words: pathophysiology, alpha-indol acetic acid, atherosclerotic cardiovascular disease, histocompatibility and deoxyribonucleic acid are just a few of the easy ones (the difference between these words and those used by legal, marketing or sales people is that these do mean something specific and concrete).

In biomedical research I must admit that it is the term 'multifactorial' that probably masks our ignorance the most. A disease or a process that is multifactorial is a disease or a process of which we know almost nothing, except that it implies the existence of many intricate pathways hidden by the action of many factors. The concepts behind the word are even more difficult to grasp than we once thought. Each new discovery uncovers the presence of additional secret codes. Our quest is now to decipher these mysterious codes.

The Heart Attack Connection

We have identified only a few of the multiple causative factors of heart disease. In some rare instances, atherosclerotic heart disease is a unifactorial, monogenic disease. Such is the case with familial hypercholesterolaemia (FH), the disease due to variations occurring in the gene coding for the low-density lipoprotein (LDL) receptor, a blood-circulating particle involved in cholesterol transport and metabolism. FH is an autosomal dominant disease that results in the presence of elevated blood-cholesterol levels.

Even though it is a monogenic disease, its manifestations are numerous. In some instances, it is fatal: people affected by a severe form of FH die of heart attacks between the ages of five and twenty-five. Even a completely fat-free diet does not counteract the genetic effects. The cholesterol produced by the organism's own liver is already too much: it deposits in arterial walls, obstructs arteries and provokes a myocardial infarction. In other cases, sufferers of FH are fine and live a normal life span, presumably because of the protective effects of certain as yet undiscovered genes.

We have to face the facts: even when heart disease is the expression of a monogenic disease, several phenomena come into play to modulate (they can alleviate as well as aggravate the symptoms) the effects of the major causative factor – an LDL-receptor abnormality.

The phenotypic manifestation of FH is seen in only one specific type of cardiovascular disease. In most cases, however, heart disease is multifactorial in origin, and there may be as many types of heart disease as there are families at risk, each one the result of a particular combination of causative factors.

Epidemiological studies (carried out on very large numbers of patients and controls), as well as family and twin studies, have unambiguously proved the inheritability of heart disease. This is why we knew from the start that we could apply the methodologies of molecular genetics. The results of the most advanced lines of investigation back up the observations that have been made over the years and the intuitive conclusions that have been drawn. We are all aware, for example, of the existence of families at higher risk, where several members have suffered from heart disease.

Besides the existence of hereditary components, the same scientific experiments have also demonstrated the presence of other, non-genetic factors: that is, environmental factors.

The development of atherosclerosis depends on how the organism copes with the lipids that circulate in the bloodstream and are taken up by the various tissues of the body. The organism of a healthy person hosts a multitude of biochemical reactions; these are the expressions of the genetic make-up and are modulated by the effects of the environment; their global action is to prevent efficiently cholesterol from depositing in arterial walls.

The respective parts played by genetic and environmental factors are often difficult to differentiate in epidemiological studies. When large-scale investigations were started two or three decades ago with the goal of evaluating the prevalence of cardiovascular disease throughout the world, it was clear, for example, that atherosclerotic heart disease was rare among the Japanese – an observation that was reported by many independent researchers. At that time many people jumped quickly to the conclusion that seemed obvious: Japanese people were somehow 'genetically' protected from heart attack. This hypothesis was further tested with several types of additional studies and was later proved wrong.

A clear-cut and elegant demonstration came with the assessment of the prevalence of heart disease among Japanese living in three different geographical and cultural environments: Japan, Hawaii and America. In Japan the people lived their traditional way of life, with a diet based on fish and vegetables. In Hawaii, an American state located half-way between Japan and America, they kept some of their traditions while adapting to a certain extent to some aspects of the American way of life. In America they had adopted a totally American life style, which included enriched foods and hamburgers. The results clearly show that the Hawaii-based Japanese are more prone to heart disease than their Japan-based counterparts, and that the American Japanese suffered a prevalence of heart disease similar to that found among a random American population. The conclusion is that the Japanese are not protected against the effects of heart disease by genetic factors but by their diet – a finding confirmed by more recent research. The incidence of heart disease has drastically increased over the past ten years or so among the inhabitants of the major Japanese cities, and this is due to a new cultural trend: it is fashionable now to eat beef and related meat produces.

Similarly, the incidence of heart disease among Indians living in Britain, although they have not changed their eating habits, is much higher than that of the inhabitants of rural India. The problem here has been identified as psychological: stressors such as racism, living far away from home, difficulties adapting to a new cultural environment and a more important work load exert a major influence on the development of heart disease in this population. An identical phenomenon had been documented within India itself, where farmers migrating to larger cities suffer from greatly increased risks of heart attack. In both cases, the usual risk factors such as cholesterol levels, hypertension and smoking have been ruled out. Indians thus seem very sensitive to, and display a strong reaction towards, the effect of psychological factors.

Cancer Is Like Heart Disease

As with heart disease, both genetic and environmental factors act in concert to induce the many forms of cancer.

We know today that some cancers are strictly hereditary (such is the case with retinoblastoma, a very rare type of eye cancer) and that some others appear in individuals who show a certain variable predisposition. There are families who are at higher risk from cancer as there are families at higher risk from heart disease.

The very idea of predisposition to a complex disease always suggests the existence of several distinct factors. Colon cancer provides a good model to understand the meaning of predisposing factors. In America it affects about 150,000 people each year, of whom 60,000 die from its consequences. Recent advances made at the molecular level indicate that this type of cancer involves the malfunction of three or four suspected genes, coupled with abnormalities induced by as yet undetermined environmental factors. These latter probably include a dietary component, since a fat-rich diet is known to be associated with an increased prevalence of the cancer, as are strong spices.

Scientists have identified one of the three or four suspected genes. Located on chromosome 7, this particular gene encodes a protein called p53 that could very well be a tumour-suppressor.

Mutations in this gene would then prevent it from performing its function.

The development of cancers depends on how well the organism copes with internal or external aggressions affecting the normal processes of controlled cell division. When, for any number of reasons, both hereditary and environmental, the mechanisms of cell division are impaired, a random cell proliferation takes place and leads to the growth of a tumour.

As in the example of heart disease, epidemiologists often have difficulties determining the respective roles of Nature and Nurture. Such has been the case in the determination of the prevalence of rhinopharyngeal cancer (throat cancer) among the Chinese. Rhinopharyngeal cancer is caused by the action of a particular virus called Epstein-Barr virus (EBV). EBV belongs to the family of herpes-causing viruses and is also implicated in the onset of another type of cancer known as Burkitt lymphoma. Rhinopharyngeal cancer indiscriminately affects individuals from all ethnic groups, irrespective of geographical location, but its incidence is particularly high among the Hans, an ethnic group representing over 90 per cent of the population of the People's Republic of China, while it is much lower among the country's many other ethnic communities. Hans who have left their country to settle in other parts of the world are equally affected by rhinopharyngeal cancer. The conclusion drawn was that genetic factors predisposed the Hans to the disease. That was until scientists discovered the real cause. When they live in other countries, the Hans do not modify their eating habits. Their regular diet includes food items which contain high levels of components known as phorbol diesters – agents facilitating EBV infections. The deleterious effect of phorbol diesters has also been demonstrated in the onset of rhinopharyngeal cancer in other populations at risk, found in North Africa and in Greenland.

Mental Illnesses

The triggering and progression of mental illnesses also depends on imbalances in the finely tuned interactions between hereditary and environmental components. The evolution of the processes implicated in a mental disease depends on the ability of the brain's biochemical mechanisms to function properly despite aggravating stress factors that comprise emotional and physical trauma, as well as miscellaneous other damaging agents such as infections or even allergies.

Very little is known about mental illnesses because the brain is the most difficult and complex organ to study. While only a few genes are expressed as proteins in other organs of the body, 40 per cent of the total number of the genes of hereditary material are specifically expressed in the brain – which explains the complexity of the phenomena occurring in our heads. Molecular neurophysiology is the field that will see the most striking advances in the near future; this is also believed to be the way forward for psychiatry.

Collating All the Results

All the illnesses that we are now starting to interpret make apparent as never before the diverse, major functions of the body. We have the means not only to alter the once inexorable course of disease but also to prevent it and to modulate the effects of our hereditary material.

With the study of heart disease, we have gathered extensive knowledge of several interconnected disorders, of which athero-sclerosis, hypertension and diabetes form the frontline targets for the elaboration of more efficient forms of treatment, for possible cures and for better prevention. We are also able to elucidate the mechanisms involved in the proper handling of cholesterol, fats, sugar and salt, in blood pressure regulation and in blood-vessel maintenance by the body. Molecular abnormalities responsible for the existence of cancers give us clues about the precise choreography of cell division and the growth and development of the organism. Alzheimer's disease presents some characteristics offering suggestions as to the general phenomenon of ageing. The effects of the gene causing ataxia telangiectasia stand at the interface between the mechanisms underlying some cancers and ageing, thereby conveying the idea of a possible relationship between the two in some instances. Schizophrenia appears as an open door leading to the intricate galleries of the labyrinth of brain function.

We have to define what is feasible and what is not. For example, if the conquest of heart disease and of cancer seems nearer every day, immortality remains unreachable. How far will we be able to go in the comprehension of brain function? Is it possible to understand how our brain works with our brain itself as the ultimate tool? In this case, it is tempting, as a counterargument, to speculate that computers will one day be able to do the trick, but this is a sloppy and self-indulgent way to leave reality. Computers are human brainchildren, and to assume that they will eventually self-organize into complex structures able to analyse (and therefore dominate us) remains pure fantasy, to be kept within the realms of science fiction.

We need to count on ourselves, accepting that the knowledge gained
in the near future will yield practical information to help us answer
these and any other questions.

Behaviour: The Way We Are

Behaviour represents a fuzzy concept encompassing all actions
undertaken by an organism in response to given sets of environmental conditions, as well as to inner feelings triggered by an
imbalance of the organism's functioning. An amalgam of the effect
of primary pulsions dictated by the palaeocortex (or the brain part
inherited from our lower animal ancestors) and more sophisticated
thought processes originating in the neocortex (evolutionarily newer,
higher-functioning brain part), behaviour is influenced by learning
and memory.

The manifestations of behaviour, a characteristic of all living organisms, and of character traits, typically human features, conform to the
general model of interplay between Nature and Nurture, although
we have little empirical evidence describing the interactions between
the two. In fact, we are at a loss to know how to design efficient
experimental tricks to allow the identification of the molecular
backbone of temper or character. Gross behavioural abnormalities
resulting from mental illnesses constitute unique ways to define
the biochemical and neurophysiological pathways implicated in the
nurturing of behaviour traits.

As of now, we can formulate our general perception of behaviour by stating that the genetic blueprint orchestrates organized
and elaborate biochemical reactions, used as moulds for biological
functions, modulated by the effects of the environment. The scope of
this preliminary model is vast, so consequently this meaning is vague,
but we do have to start somewhere if we want to progress. We can
take a first step by looking at what we have learned about a subject
intimately related to behaviour and character – intelligence.

The Tricky Problem of Intelligence

Intelligence is a typical multifactorial product of the grey matter of the
brain's neocortex and the archetype of higher cortical functions.

A definition of 'intelligence' is difficult to express simply. The
Webster's II New Riverside Dictionary describes it as 'the capacity
to learn and solve problems and difficulties', as well as 'superior
mental powers'. In fact, intelligence assumes many forms, including

overlapping aspects such as abstract, mathematical and practical skills, ability to formulate, analyse and synthesize, imagination and creativity (as, for example, in music, poetry, literature, painting, sculpture and science), social and communication talents, pattern recognition, learning and memory, and sensitivity. Quite a mosaic of functions!

Discussions about intelligence invariably raise sensitive issues, and people are often quite uncomfortable talking about it. Western cultures consider higher intelligence to be the ultimate form of superiority: after all, it is grey matter that puts us proudly at the top of the pyramid of evolution.

There is, however, a sizable problem: what do we mean by 'higher intelligence'? Higher compared to what? We have no tangible frame of reference, no point of comparison, apart from subjective value judgements. Or maybe this is not true. We do have at our disposal a unique, concrete way of quantifying intelligence: the intelligence quotient (or infamous IQ). An IQ test contains a number of questions and problems that need solving within a limited time. Individual performance is measured by a score called IQ: the better the performance in the test, the higher the IQ value. The mean IQ value in the general population, which is also the value scored by the largest number of people, is arbitrarily defined as 100. The distribution of IQ values occurs within a fairly narrow range – roughly between 70 and 130 – although a smaller number of individuals score out of these limits. Albert Einstein, for example, is said to have had an IQ of 170; Goethe, 200.

The IQ test was invented by the French psychologist Alfred Binet in response to a request from the French Ministry of Education at the beginning of this century. Binet was once asked what IQ represented with respect to intelligence and answered, 'But IQ is what my test measures!' Nothing else. Indeed, strictly speaking, a person with a high IQ is a person who performs well on an IQ test, therefore obtaining a high score. Any other interpretation of IQ values is speculative and involves often questionable extrapolations. Nevertheless, IQ measurement remains the widely accepted tool to quantify highly developed thought processes.

The question of whether heredity or cultural environment plays a major role in the development and expression of intelligence has triggered passionate debates over the years. Not surprisingly, geneticists and environmentalists have now reached an honourable compromise, with proof that intelligence, as measured by IQ tests, results from the interplay of genetic and environmental components.

Many epidemiological studies conducted over the past few decades support this conclusion, but two published in the last four years stand out clearly and unambiguously because of their impeccable approach: one is the Colorado Adoption Project and the other, the French Adoption Study.

Genetics studies of adopted children are invaluable sources of information. Adoption means that children born from their genitors, the biological parents, are raised in the different environment of their adoptive parents. Children brought up by their biological parents live in a milieu conflating both genetic and environmental influences; under these conditions, it is difficult to assess the precise cause of a given trait of family resemblance. An adopted child, however, grows in the environment of a family with completely different genetic traits; here environmental influences play a dominant role in the development of the child.

In the Colorado Adoption Project, 245 adopted children, representatives of a white, urban, American population, were followed for eight consecutive years. Their IQs, as well as those from both their biological and adopted parents, were measured at regular intervals. The conclusions of the study revealed that until the age of three or four the IQs of the adopted children were similar to the IQs of their adoptive parents. Later, however, their IQs change progressively, so that the older they become, the more their IQs resemble the IQs of their biological parents.

The investigators were able to determine the precise value of a variable known in genetics as the heritability coefficient (for those who are interested, this was 0.36). The heritability coefficient permits us to prove whether genetic or environmental factors, or both, play a role in the familial transmission of any given feature. The determination of its value is important to geneticists. It does not quantify the respective influences of the two types of factors, but we can say from the results of the Colorado Adoption Project that the part played by heredity is high in the transmission of IQ but environmental factors also have an important role. This is a vague statement, but it does reconcile the views of both camps.

The French Adoption Study also wanted to determine IQ values of adopted children. Moreover, it took into account high versus low socioeconomic status (SES) of both the biological and the adoptive families. The results of the study demonstrated the action of two major effects in the inheritance of the IQ trait. The first was due to the action of genetic factors: the average IQ of adoptees with high SES biological parents was fifteen points higher than the average IQ of adoptees with low SES biological parents. The second was due to the part played by the environment: the IQ of children adopted by high SES parents was twelve points higher than the IQ of children adopted by low SES parents.

In conclusion, both genetic and environmental influences operate in the mechanisms of intelligence as measured by IQ, but no study provides an explanation for the respective parts played by either one – a challenge for someone to take up!

We know that the performance of an individual on IQ tests is consistent only over short periods of time and changes at different stages of development. It is quite possible that each of the two influences plays a different role at different times. Examples abound of children who are successful in primary school but become failures in university systems, and vice versa. Under adverse conditions, such as severe famine, environment plays the major role (and heredity is negligible) because brain development is entirely impaired by nutrient deficiencies.

Children with dietary deficiencies would certainly improve their intellectual (as well as physical) development by being given supplements of nutrients they lack. Such could be the case of vitamins. This is what could be advocated from studies whose results have been severely criticized. Much noise has surrounded the announcement that a cocktail of twenty-three vitamins and minerals representing 100 per cent of the American recommended daily allowance increases IQ among children. Many flaws, however, both in data analysis and in result interpretation, as well as flashy, ensuing, publicity campaign should invalidate the conclusions offered from this study. What the authors tried to suggest on the basis of their results (that all children should eat 100 per cent US RDA vitamin doses to become more intelligent) is premature at best, and reprehensible at the worst. The most important message that comes out of these studies is that supplying vitamins to children with deficiencies may be important – which we already knew from other research programmes. At this point, what we need is to find a way of identifying the children whose IQ would benefit from vitamin supplements.

In the development of intelligence, as in the case of other human features, it seems sensible to put forward the view that Nature exerts its influence *via* Nurture. Indeed, success at school is generally taken as a measure of intelligence. A child who performs well in abstract disciplines such as mathematics, who participates constructively in intellectual exchanges, who does his or her homework on time and who is one year ahead of his or her peers will certainly be stamped as 'bright' or 'intelligent'. Such a child will naturally be pushed towards a good university, while another who, for whatever reason, fails early on will probably not be given that chance.

The amount of pressure applied by family or teachers on a child so that he or she obtains high grades constitutes a strong catalyst to the expression of the child's natural capabilities. The higher the achievement, the more supportive and encouraging the family will be. The child then adds confidence to demonstrated competence, which compels him or her to choose more challenging classes. Successful people benefit from ever-increasing intellectual stimulation and are thus able to select their own conditions of environment. Too great a pressure, however, can be a double-edged sword, and the individual becomes what is called an overachiever. The associated features of the syndrome of overachievement are not enviable. True, overachievers are successful in certain areas and therefore admired, but these persons are also likely to be regarded with suspicion, which, together with the fact they are never satisfied with their accomplishments (however impressive these may be), generally leads to social and emotional difficulties and the psychiatrist's couch!

In the control of the development of intelligence, as for heart disease, hypertension and cancer, the message once again is one of balance and moderation. If I were a moralist, I would insist on the importance of using, but not abusing, good things. But then we are left with a cruel dilemma, forced to choose between either a long and dull or a short and exciting life. Roll on the long and exciting one!

15 _____

Why Are Diseases So Common?
Because of Life's Complexity

'WHY ARE DISEASES SO COMMON?' THIS LEGITIMATE QUESTION IS ONE
that we ask hopelessly while fearing the seemingly random attacks
of debilitating and lethal illness. In this chapter I will look at
all types of inherited disorders – that is, ones transmitted from
generation to generation according to the laws of classical genetics
– as well as those resulting from interactions between hereditary
and environmental factors whose mode of inheritance remains a
mystery.

Selective Advantages Are Conserved
Throughout Evolution

Studies of genetic markers reveal how much the DNA molecule is
a dynamic system constantly pushed by evolutionary pressure to
modify itself. During the continuous processes of DNA replication
and duplication, of cell division and of egg formation, mutations
arise spontaneously, creating a whole range of modifications that
are conserved if they happen to confer a selective advantage at that
particular time. We stand here right at the heart of Darwin's theory
of evolution; one of the basic principles is that a selective advantage
is the fundamental requirement for survival of the fittest. Mutations,
genotype and its phenotypic manifestations, and the interactions
between Nature and Nurture play key parts in the evolution of
living species.

   Physical and behavioural traits bestowing selective advantages
are not only conserved by the mechanisms of evolution; they are
also selected for. Natural selection operates to keep the organism
that is best adapted to its environment, encouraging the prevalence
of a particularly beneficial attribute. Thus, for example, when

climatic conditions led to increasing desertification, with only the top branches of taller trees bearing foliage, the extraordinary long neck of the giraffe constituted a selective advantage: the giraffe had adapted to changing conditions of the environment; it could thus eat and survive.

Obviously the giraffe's long neck did not appear one day out of the blue as the result of a single, isolated mutation. Rather, it is the consequence of thousands of DNA variations that have taken place progressively over thousands of years in a concerted fashion.

The converse of selective advantage is also true. Traits conferring deleterious effects to the individual (and therefore to the survival of its species) are simply eliminated throughout evolution. An organism unfit to live in a particular environment is an organism with features not adapted for that milieu; it will not survive and the traits disappear.

This brief sketch of the theory of evolution is an oversimplification of what happens in reality. The effects of particular genotype modifications – whether advantageous or disadvantageous at any given time – are modified by the presence of other genotypic particularities, the nature of the corresponding phenotypic manifestations and the changing conditions of the environment. We also need to keep in mind that evolution is a dynamic process. It corresponds to a tendency towards equilibrium that takes thousands of years to achieve and that can never ultimately be reached because of the constant changes and interplay between all the variables (genotype, phenotype and environment).

The Benefit of a Disease

Physical and behavioural characteristics displayed by a living organism come from an array of situations to which the organism has had to adapt. Those which could not adapt in time have become extinct. This is why the evolutionary benefit of many human features appears at first sight difficult to explain. This is especially true of the inherited molecular mechanisms underlying disease. A rational explanation, however, lies at the root of the illness. We must seek the meaning of the existence of a disease not in the expressed, observable phenotype but in the biochemical reactions directed by the genotype of the individual. The real answer concerns the concepts of evolution and natural selection. Sickle cell anaemia provides the best-known example.

Sickle cell anaemia, as mentioned earlier, is a form of extremely severe anaemia necessitating regular blood transfusions. Its clinical manifestations include red blood cell aggregation in blood vessels, inducing ulcerations and infarcts of the skin, liver, lung, spleen and bones, and intense, acute pain. Yet the frequency of the disease is so high among some populations (the prevalence of the trait of sickle cell anaemia reaches 40 per cent in some African countries) that this trait – if the theory of evolution is correct – must confer a selective advantage. This is at first unbelievable; what could possibly be the benefit of a disease, of suffering?

We know now that the answer is not to do with the peripheric, directly observable manifestations, but with the cellular expression of the disease. As extraordinary as it may seem, sickle cell anaemia does grant a selective edge for survival: it protects the affected individual against malaria. Malaria is an infectious disease caused by a small parasite, a haematozoan called *Plasmodium falciparum*, which develops in the red blood cells of humans. The parasite cannot live and multiply in the red blood cells of a patient suffering from sickle cell anaemia, because the presence of abnormal haemoglobin molecules – the cause of the disease – induces biochemical modifications in the environment of the cell that are incompatible with the parasite's requirements. This is why the beta-globin gene carrying the mutation responsible for sickle cell anaemia is particularly frequent in equatorial and Mediterranean countries where malaria is endemic.

Heart Disease: An Invaluable Asset for Our Prehistoric Ancestors

What follows in the next sections is speculation. It has been backed up by neither tangible, scientific evidence nor empirical observations. Nevertheless, suppositions that are based on sound theories constitute working hypotheses worth pursuing. They also allow temporary escape from the rigid framework of exact sciences, giving us the chance to engage in a different type of creativity. Besides, they are interesting – not that this is any excuse!

In the Western world cardiovascular disease is by far the leading cause of death and invalidity, and its toll is mounting in the Third World. It most frequently takes the form of atherosclerotic heart disease, or heart disease due to cholesterol deposition in arteries. What can possibly be the selective advantage of a trait with such severe clinical manifestations that it is the number-one killer?

In order to understand where we come from, we need to look far back into prehistoric times, tens of thousands of years ago. As far as we know, the regular diet of our prehistoric ancestors consisted of fruits, leaves and roots. Meat was probably an extremely rare treat, and the killing of a mammoth was such an exceptional event that it justified the painting of faithful representations, a few of which have defied the erosion of time and are still visible today. No one added salt or butter to improve the taste of their food. Moreover, the days that brought meals must have been limited; snowy winters would have been very hard to get through.

Prehistoric people had to adapt to the adverse conditions of their environment. It took tens of thousands of years, but their organisms developed an enzymatic machinery that allowed them to store as efficiently as possible the energy eked out of meagre and scarce rations. They had no choice but to store that energy in the form of fat. We are the direct descendants of those people who slowly geared their metabolism towards most efficient forms of fat storage.

However, we have modified our environment over the last two or three centuries (a very short time in the evolutionary scale), and today in the Western world food is in excess. The profusion of enriched food that we have voluntarily introduced to our diet is turning against us, because we have not had the time to adapt to this brutal change in eating habits. Most of the people who die today from atherosclerotic heart attacks would probably be the best at tolerating the harsh food conditions of prehistoric times. Thus a trait (resulting from a combination of the effects of many genes) that was advantageous a long time ago turns out to be deleterious today.

Other Modern Diseases

The same reasoning could hold true for diabetes. This is a devastating disease when we eat but an advantage during periods of starvation.

Hypertension, the silent killer, is also a very common illness causing cardiovascular disease. The mechanisms controlling blood-pressure regulation are thrown off balance by too much salt in the diet or by failures in adapting to the stress of modern life. Yet these very mechanisms, and in particular adrenaline boosts in the bloodstream, must have served specific purposes. Here again we can propose a rational and reasonable explanation, suggesting that these same mechanisms are indispensable for improved alertness, for readiness to fight and defend oneself, and for being quicker to escape danger – qualities that would undeniably have contributed to the prolonging of our prehistoric ancestors' lives, constantly on the alert, as they would have been, against predators of all kinds.

As for allergies, the hypersensitivity of the organism to allergens is an extreme form of response whose underlying mechanisms are indispensable for the defence of the organism against viruses, bacteria, parasites and foreign molecules that continuously invade the body. Without these defence mechanisms, animals and humans would never have survived the repeated attacks and invasions of pathogens of all kinds throughout evolution.

Just as with allergies, cancers are the consequence of impaired regulations of vital cellular functions. Here these functions allow the cells of the body to divide and to proliferate. When, for reasons we are only starting to understand, cell division escapes the finely tuned control mechanisms, the ensuing random proliferation of cancer cells yields abnormal structures such as cancerous tumours.

How about mental illness? What purpose, for example, could the schizophrenia trait serve? Indeed, if schizophrenia in any ethnic group affects about 1 per cent of all individuals, the underlying traits are even more prevalent – up to 10 per cent, according to many investigators. There is of course no general agreement as to the evolutionary reason for the trait, but several hypotheses have been advanced. For example, schizophrenic individuals, as well as patients displaying milder forms of the disease and suffering from what are called schizoid personalities, often show great artistic talent, in particular in the fields of drawing, painting and poetry. Since they lose their ability to differentiate the self from the non-self, they are also attracted by mystical experiences. They hear voices and can thus claim to be guided by some superior power, ordering them to execute particular actions. There is a theory that schizophrenic individuals could have served as sorcerers and wizards in primitive societies.

These thoughts are only general observations and should be handled with great care. In no way can they be used, for example, to suggest that all artists and religious adepts present some form or some traits of schizophrenia. However, until proved wrong, they need not be discarded, because they constitute working hypotheses, even though some of them, I admit, would be very difficult to formulate in a systematic and scientific fashion. They do, though, offer the comforting thought that disease is not a random strike of adverse forces but the inevitable consequence of millions of years of evolution, intertwined with sudden environmental and cultural modifications. They also indicate that seemingly deleterious traits have served specific purposes during the process of evolution, and that humans would not be as they are if these traits had not been transmitted over countless generations.

Complexity of Organization and the Mystery of the Force

The understanding of the multifactorial features of human beings, such as behaviour and character traits or diseases of complex aetiology, is the most fascinating goal of current biomedical research. An understanding of the intricacy of the components involved is the prelude to our gaining the power to forge proper tools to improve the human condition.

Whether we will one day be able to comprehend fully the complex machinery of a living organism so that we can develop efficient means of intervention is open to debate. Indeed, although it appears that eventually research will permit the identification of most (if not all) components, the overall puzzle will still not be unravelled. Interplay between the respective pieces will trigger additional properties and generate further orders of complexity that we cannot even imagine now. The overall, observed effect of a disease or of a character trait is qualitatively and quantitatively stronger than the sum of the isolated parts, be they genetic or environmental. For this reason, we must reject the idea of a deterministic, oversimplified conceptualization when we analyse the processes of life.

In our current state of knowledge, we assume that living organisms obey classical laws of physics; this is what molecular biology has confirmed. A purely deterministic view would thus tend to reduce life to a unique mathematical expression or to a collection of mathematical solutions. If only because of technical difficulties, that remains impossible.

Classical mathematics and physics resolve continuous phenomena by providing solutions to the equations that best describe these phenomena. Life's processes are amenable to such a treatment because they represent continuous events. The growth of an organ and of the whole body, cell proliferation, progressive cholesterol deposition in arteries, DNA replication, blood-pressure variations and biochemical transformations of organic molecules represent continuous variations taking place constantly in different parts of the body. A total analysis of an organism would consist of determining a set of mathematical expressions for all simultaneous reactions occurring in the body at a given time, and then of calculating the combined solution of the millions of equations involved. Even if we could assimilate all the biochemical and physiological reactions to simplified mathematical functions, the most powerful computers around could never resolve such a complex set of functions.

Life on earth presupposes three fundamental, interrelated behaviour traits: complexity, cooperativity and self-organization. A living organism is the result of the aggregation of organic molecules; inert and featureless matter has been converted into a self-organized structure in which cooperativity between the basic component molecules confers a mysterious state exhibiting life's features. We are at a loss to explain the nature of this mysterious state. Imagine a game that involves gathering all the component atoms of a human being (mainly carbon, oxygen, hydrogen, nitrogen, phosphorus, calcium, potassium and rarer oligo-elements) and shaking them together. We could shake them for a very long time, heat them or submit them to electric or magnetic currents, but would not manage to create a man or a woman. Yet these atoms are what we are all made of, as are earth, wood and other animals. It is just that they have been ordered and self-organized into the precise arrangement of a living human being.

We have to admit the existence of a qualitative jump from a mixture of inert atoms and molecules to elaborate states displaying sophisticated activities and behaviour – a jump from the mineral to the living world. This jump is what is commonly referred to as 'the life force'. The complexity reaches its peak with the emergence of the epitome of higher functions – thought processes – although the human brain itself is composed of the same atoms as the remainder of the body. This is why we also have to admit the reality of another qualitative jump between lower animals and humans.

We have been aware of complexity and self-organization for a long time, and not only in biology but also in physics, cosmology and computer science. Just think of a snowflake falling slowly and noiselessly on a pane of glass. It follows no predictable pattern when it metamorphoses into a unique, symmetrical crystal; the difference between it and a human being, however, is that the spontaneously self-organized ice crystal, despite its elaborate design, remains a lifeless thing.

The world as we see it today is the consequence of unidirectional, organized growth. Whether this growth is predetermined or takes place spontaneously over time is a major philosophical and scientific debate. The progressive organization occurs at all levels of complexity as far as we can see. Whether or not the Big Bang theory is correct, most physicists agree that the universe arose from a featureless state, from nothing, 4.5 billion years ago. Life has developed over 3.5

billion years, starting with simpler life forms such as viruses and bacteria and progressively evolving up to humans. At the beginning, simpler genes probably coded for simple proteins with unique activities and functions. Both the genes and their corresponding proteins then became larger assemblies of increasing complexity, so that unique molecules displayed multiple functions. Different protein chains coded by different genes have also assembled into structures of many subunits where the various subunits act in a cooperative fashion to confer enhanced functional properties (this is the case with the human haemoglobin molecule, formed by the aggregation of four protein chains, and earthworm haemoglobin, composed of about 150 protein subunits).

Life, however, remains a paradox. We describe and conceptualize physical phenomena with theories rooted in the branch of physics known as thermodynamics, whose principles were established in the nineteenth century. To the best of our knowledge, the universe is ruled by the laws contained in the second principle of thermodynamics. In particular this principle describes a fundamental quantity known as entropy, and states that entropy can at best remain stable (as in a completely closed and isolated system – which cannot exist, because the universe is a constant exchange of energy between the plethora of systems that constitute it). Thus in a collection of interacting systems constantly exchanging energy (such as the world and the universe), entropy can only increase, and an increase in entropy means a state of greater chaos.

What is entropy? It is because of entropy that a waterfall always goes downwards, that a river does not flow from the sea up to the top of the mountain, that an abandoned building is condemned to decay and that, after death, a body returns to dust. To retard the process of entropy, one must spend energy, as in repairing an old house or car. However, despite the energy expended, global entropy is still increasing. Any physical structure thus seems destined to move towards disorganization.

Life represents a transitional state, defying the laws of entropy. The passage from fertilized egg to foetus to adult corresponds to ever-increasing organization – not what would have been predicted according to the second principle of thermodynamics. Since we have so far been unable to reconcile entropy with our behaving in constructive ways, we have had to introduce magic in the form of what is called 'the life force'. But we need not cite magic to explain life's processes. Many scientists believe that organization into living systems results from what is most difficult to comprehend – its complexity. Complexity is not an accident encountered in a few instances; it is a general quality displayed at all levels in the universe, from molecules to galaxies.

We know that the established laws of thermodynamics are correct and unquestionable. As commonly accepted, the whole universe is expanding, slowly sliding towards a state of greater chaos; our theories predict that it will terminate in a heat death. The effects of complexity, however, could very well counterbalance this apparently inexorable course. Complexity was once believed to be too complicated to be analysed with calculations. New mathematical formulations, however, are being developed today for the treatment of both complexity and chaos. A report from 1989 (awaiting confirmation) has provided the first clue that the solar system – the sun and its nine planets – behave in a chaotic rather than a quasi-periodic fashion, and that planet trajectories could be accurately predicted within a time frame of 10 million years. It is tempting to hope that out of increased complexity and chaos an as yet unsuspected self-organization could emerge, leading not to the ultimate disappearance of the universe but its replacement by a more elaborate structure. Since we are at the frontier between science, speculation and science fiction, we can ask whether living organisms will not ultimately self-organize into configurations exhibiting new orders of complexity – a line of reasoning that coincides with other philosophical speculations, such as Nietzsche's idea of the superman.

In conclusion, we should return to sounder scientific thought. Today scientific fashion insists on the elaboration of theories that permit the integration of different disciplines. In the near future, the elucidation of complex systems will enable us to draw parallels between all phenomena of this type and integrate them into comprehensive and universal models. The role of molecular biology is to unravel the complexity of the genetic blueprints of all living systems.

16

Biotechnology: Key Investment of the Future or Giant Flop?

SINCE THE END OF THE 1970s ENTREPRENEURS, MOSTLY AMERICAN, have been quick to realize the astounding money-making potential of biotechnology products. They foresaw that speculative investments in this general area were capable of generating quick returns. So they created a new type of company, the biotechnology company, entirely modelled on computer companies — quite a role model to follow!

How did biotechnology companies start and how have they managed to retain the popularity they enjoyed from the beginning? After all, they usually operate only on the basis of an idea, not on the solid ground of an already existing product. There are several possibilities for a management who wishes to obtain the money required to start a biotechnology company. Funds are raised through the system of venture capital; from private investors (Research and Development limited partnerships), who benefit from the associated tax shelters, although these tend to fade away; from large sums of money provided by traditional pharmaceutical giants, who create for themselves an easy opening into the biotechnology arena; and also from federal research grants.

Money-making Dreams

The phenomenal amounts of money necessary to carry out biotechnology's research operations have not deterred investors from this new type of venture. This is why, following in the footsteps of south San Francisco's role model, Genentech, the first company to specialize in biotechnology, more than 400 companies of the same type, although smaller in size, have been started in the past eleven years and more than $10 billion invested. Raising the money was a relatively easy task initially, in the late 1970s. The general feeling then was that anybody creating a biotechnology company would succeed rapidly. The 1970s and early 1980s were indeed very exciting times and there was a firm belief that original ideas from young, bright scientists were guaranteed to earn huge profits very quickly.

If the model of the computer industry held, a young person could hope to become a multimillionaire after transforming his or her house's backyard into a product-oriented research laboratory.

Since those early, heady days a hard lesson has been learned. There was a problem no one had thought of, due to the basic difference between a biotechnology product and a product from the computer industry. Computer software or a computer chip does not take very long to reach the marketplace – a matter of weeks. This is not the case with biotechnology. The prototype of a biotechnology product is a natural molecule of the body produced by genetic engineering. So far, so good. But in America the FDA, the federal organization which has to approve a drug's sale, perceives it otherwise and has decided to treat recombinant DNA proteins as conventional drugs. The result is that it takes an average of seven years to carry out the clinical trials necessary to gain approval – provided everything goes smoothly! – which means when the drug does not show unwanted side effects; when there are no toxicity problems; and when no better or cheaper drug with similar action appears at the same time.

In the business world, time is money; in biotechnology, time is a lot of money. The cost of the actual invention of a new drug is estimated at $30 million; on top of that figure, $70 million are then required to perform the clinical trials, and then there are marketing and sales costs! This hard reality makes it unsurprising that over thirty companies have folded during the first half of 1989 alone. Others have been bought by larger pharmaceutical companies. Of course, many independent companies still remain, but they face great hardship. Only the successful financial breaks of the past few years can keep them in the forefront of speculative ventures. The incredible paradox is that investors still believe in biotechnology's future and keep on feeding money into operations, which is why new biotechnology companies are started almost every week.

No Longer a Teenager, But Not Yet an Adult

Why, if the road to high returns is paved with disillusionment and deceit, does biotechnology remain a keenly sought after investment? The answer is that biotechnology will be a key technology of the future. No one can deny it. But the whole field of biotechnology has had to adjust to the attitudes of the market and of the investors. It has now entered a transitional phase and is gradually moving from teenagehood into early adulthood – a difficult but imperative move.

It is true that many of biotechnology's original aims were overambitious, but in a way this has turned out to be a major asset for young and aggressive companies: their dynamism is able to move mountains. Most biotechnology companies, however, have suffered from an excessive frenzy that has blinded their management teams to the market's harsh reality. The extraordinarily large sums of money offered to newly formed biotechnology companies have brought problems rather than providing a comfortable headstart. The most prosperous ones – in particular, those that benefited from favourable stock market prices when they became public – have grown too fast. Overexpansion has meant excessive spending on personnel, materials and buildings. The main problem was that many managements were hoping to generate healthy cash flows within short periods of time, sometimes as little as a year or two. This, of course, did not happen. Start-up companies also tended to spread themselves too thin, pursuing several research projects rather than focusing on a few possible winners.

Most companies have finally come to the conclusion that it is imperative to cut their losses and modify their long-term approaches. Practical measures involve cutting spending, reducing the number of employees, concentrating on a few research projects and signing solid financial agreements with respected pharmaceutical firms. Under such agreements, the biotechnology company is reimbursed for part or all of the research money already invested, receives funds to continue research on the product and gets 6 to 10 per cent royalties on the product sales. The pharmaceutical company, with its product development, marketing, and sales structures already in place, can afford to bring the product to the market stage. And this means that, in order to receive FDA approval, it will organize the necessary clinical trials in collaboration with respected medical centres.

Until recently, this strategy seemed enough to put a biotechnology company back on its feet, provided that the projected sales of the product under the licensing agreement were large enough: that is, more than $100 million. It is the pharmaceutical company, though, that will pocket most of the present and future earnings.

For this reason, biotechnology companies must undergo a drastic transformation. They must leave the stage of start-up companies and enter the world of pharmaceutical giants. In order to fulfil their original promise of generating high financial returns, they themselves need to become pharmaceutical-type companies. This is the meaning of 'entering adulthood'. They have little choice if they wish to survive. What will the direct consequences be? Security analysts and market experts foresee more stability in stock prices; no more of the hectic fluctuations that have characterized biotechnology's recent past! The negative aspect, however, is that we will move away from exciting scientific ideas and discoveries generated by bright young scientists and switch instead to more traditionally routine, uninspiring, activities such as marketing and legal battles. A less interesting but more stable future lies ahead and appears to be the necessary trade-off.

The transition into adulthood is much harder than it seems at first sight. More than its relatively small size, more than its low to non-existent profits, the difficulty for a biotechnology company stems from its mind set. A start-up company is lifted by the dynamism and the ideas of a few dedicated and hard-working scientists, backed up by entrepreneurial managements. An established industry is rooted in a well-organized and solid structure where sales are the pivotal concern. These two organizations involve completely different types of individuals and different types of creativity. That employee turnover among biotechnology companies has been high over the past few years does not come as a surprise. A few leaders such as Genentech, Amgen and Biogen are attempting to achieve the transition but experience the difficulties inherent in having as employees people with opposing viewpoints.

On top of everything, the patenting field adds considerable confusion. Any industry involved in the design of new products absolutely has to protect its ideas and inventions by patents. In the field of biotechnology, however, no one is able at the moment to segregate what is patentable from what is not. Besides, in several instances, distinct patents filed by different laboratories and overlapping in the use of a given drug have been issued at practically the same time. Lawsuits invariably follow any new drug approval. Biotechnology analysts fear that a strict and appropriate legislation aimed at sorting out current misunderstandings will have the disastrous effect of harming companies. Many are afraid that several patents that have already been issued will be overruled.

One thing is clear. Recombinant DNA drugs constitute a new generation of products that are of tremendous help in fighting human disease. However, they are also a commodity and, as such, are powerfully influenced by the financial world. The path from the idea of a drug to its marketing is tortuous, as demonstrated by the histories of Genentech's Activase and Amgen's Epogen.

Genentech's Activase

Activase is the tradename for tissue specific plasminogen activator (t-PA). As we have already seen, t-PA is a natural protein of the human body whose role is to dissolve blood clots in arteries and thereby prevent heart attacks. Activase belongs to the battery of new-generation drugs manufactured by genetic engineering. The human t-PA gene was isolated by a Genentech research team, as well as by several other laboratories. Genentech's scientists integrated the t-PA gene into the genetic material of bacteria, and used the transformed bacteria to produce large quantities of t-PA molecules.

The original idea was to administer a t-PA dose immediately after a myocardial infarction in order to clear the arteries of their clots and hence prevent another heart attack. Used within the four hours following a myocardial infarct, t-PA has been shown to decrease the mortality rate by half. The market is ideal, because each person is a potential candidate. In the Western world, after all, one individual out of two dies from cardiovascular disease complications. The drug was announced in a blaze of publicity in 1985 and has since then been the object of an extraordinarily successful marketing campaign.

By 1987 everybody in the biotechnology industry looked with hope at Genentech's success with t-PA. The feeling was that t-PA approval would strengthen the public's faith in biotechnology as an area worth investing in and that all biotechnology stocks would regain vigour. For a while, delays in FDA approval cast a shadow over the field and created a sense of disappointment, but t-PA approval was finally granted. By the end of 1987, Genentech's management predicted an annual market of $200 million. The company was really betting on t-PA sales to help it reach the ranks of the top pharmaceutical giants.

Activase was unfortunately not the only blood-clot-dissolving drug on the market. There was another drug, streptokinase, which had been known for several years already. It is not manufactured by genetic engineering techniques, but is another natural protein of the body. Activase was supposed to be more efficient than streptokinase – thus justifying its high single dose cost of $2,000, eleven times higher than a corresponding streptokinase dose – yet this was not proved definitively.

In April 1988 Genentech advertised sales of 2,000 Activase doses per week, up from January by a factor of two. In the months that followed no further information was released and it was assumed that the sales were continuing as anticipated. But in July 1988 rumours began that sales were lower than originally announced. According to Genentech's management, the reason was the over-stocking by distributors and hospitals, and they pretended that the demand for t-PA was continuing to increase. The situation was clarified by September: Activase purchase had been stable since April, but the actual number of weekly doses sold was 1,000, not 2,000! Evidence to corroborate this appeared two months later, when it became clear that 50,000 patients had been treated with Activase between November 1987 and October 1988, which indeed corresponded to 1,000 doses per week. By the end of September 1988, Genentech had announced the suspension of its Activase production.

That was only the beginning of the Activase episode. The public then learned that fifteen researchers participating in the clinical trials to evaluate t-PA efficiency owned Genentech stocks. Furthermore, the company had also offered stocks to three other researchers holding key positions in the evaluation process. One of them was a member of the executive committee of TIMI (Thrombolysis in Myocardial Infarction), the very committee in charge of supervising clinical testing. No less than seven lawsuits were immediately filed against Genentech by its own stockholders, on the grounds of withholding crucial information – information that was used by insiders to sell their stocks for a total value of $24 million!

One of the TIMI members admitted that the committee had been strongly biased towards the advantages of t-PA from the very start, even before clinical trials had started. Dr Victor Marder, deputy director of the Department of Hematology at Rochester University Medical Center, also indicated in a 1989 interview to *Nature* that TIMI had decided to start the second phase of mortality studies before the results of the first (whose goal was to compare the effects of t-PA and streptokinase) had been properly analysed. Streptokinase was simply ruled out of the second phase, which took away any chance of comparing the modes of action of the two drugs.

Genentech's stock price plunged from $65 to $14, and remained at the bottom even when the Dow Jones index went up again. Which has not prevented Genentech from filing for an extension of Activase to other therapeutic applications in all countries where the company has commercial antennae, nor two of its Japanese partners, Mitsubishi Kasei Corporation and Kyowa Hakko

Kogyo, from filing for Japan's Activase approval in the treatment of heart disease. In Europe, Genentech's affiliates are devoting considerable effort to carrying out clinical tests in order to convince cardiologists of t-PA's advantages. It is today commonly accepted that t-PA is a better clot-dissolving drug than streptokinase, but that its action is followed by a higher rate of formation of new blood clots.

The battle is far from being over. The pharmaceutical giant SmithKline Beecham has recently introduced on the market a modified streptokinase molecule with a more specific course of action, which has had the immediate effect of decreasing the overall price of Activase.

The latest development in the saga comes from an academic research laboratory. We have known for a long time that t-PA is active only for a relatively short time after injection, because it is rapidly inactivated in the bloodstream by specific inhibitors. These are natural molecules of the organism that stop t-PA's action; they participate in the sequence of events aimed at finely regulating what happens in the arteries. The most important of these t-PA inhibitors is called PAI-1 (plasminogen activator inhibitor-1). A t-PA molecule that is resistant to PAI-1 would have a greatly enhanced ability to dissolve blood clots. This is precisely what was achieved by a scientific team from Texas University, Dallas, led by Edwin L. Madison; their results were reported in *Nature*, 29 June 1989. This team was able to engineer a mutant t-PA molecule, or a molecule that has been slightly altered, so that although its blood-clot-dissolving properties are unchanged their sensitivity to PAI-1 attack is decreased. Thus the second t-PA generation is born, even before the controversy surrounding the first one has died down. We can safely predict that this new PAI-1 resistant t-PA molecule will have a profound impact on the benefits expected from the sale of Activase.

This is how fast things move in the drug industry. One can never rest on an apparently original invention. In this case, it is clear that Genentech's officials showed an exaggerated enthusiasm for their miracle drug t-PA. The drug's therapeutic properties were overestimated, embarrassing data were omitted and key information was withheld. I have encountered similar situations many times in biotechnology companies, where the product becomes what the management wants it to be rather than what it really is. Distorted information is fed to the media, as the company can hide behind secrecy agreements and patent protection. It can divulge what seems best suited to its own interests. The press feels understandably manipulated and is beginning to vent its frustration against the whole field of biotechnology.

Amgen's EPO

Biotechnology companies are also facing other types of problems, stemming from the need to protect their products with patents. They are frequently faced with the difficult situation of having to defend their rights through damaging court battles, as Amgen knows only too well.

Amgen was a big favourite among investors a couple of years ago. Its latest award-winning drug, human erythropoietin (EPO), obtained FDA approval. EPO is a natural protein produced by the kidneys, and its role in the body is to stimulate red blood cell production. The gene coding for the EPO protein was isolated for the first time in 1983 by an Amgen research team, while several other laboratories were working along similar lines. At that time, Amgen's lead was so widely publicized that many of its competitors decided to stop their studies of the EPO gene.

Its ability to boost the formation of red blood cells makes EPO a perfect drug to fight anaemia. Amgen's proposed applications for this drug included anaemia associated with some cancers, anaemia associated with AIDS treatment, and reduction of the need for blood transfusions among patients suffering from chronic renal failure and requiring regular dialysis. EPO's annual market could very well amount to $100 million during the first year of the drug's release into the marketplace, and then gradually reach $1 billion within a few years. That would make it the most successful new drug. So, everything is fine? Not at all. Amgen is fighting legal battles on two fronts: against one of its competitors, Genetics Institute Inc., and against its own commercial partner, the powerful pharmaceutical company Johnson & Johnson.

Genetics Institute Inc., backed up by Chugai-Upjohn (the result of a joint venture between the Japanese company Chugai Pharmaceutical Co. and the Kalamazoo, Michigan-based Upjohn Co.), was granted a patent covering the use of the EPO molecule in July 1987, while Amgen's patent, issued a few months later, protected only the process to manufacture EPO by genetic engineering. The confusion arose because two separate committees had evaluated the two patent applications. Amgen feels frustrated and advocates that it should be granted all the rights to EPO because it was first in the race to clone its gene.

Realizing how many laboratories had worked at the same time

on the EPO project reinforces the commonly held opinion that good ideas in the field of biotechnology are never original. I have often heard molecular biologists say that if a researcher has a new idea, he or she can be sure that hundreds of other researchers have come up with the same idea at the same time, and that probably dozens of others have already had it before. It therefore comes as no surprise to find that Amgen had the unpleasant surprise of hearing Genetics Institute Inc. receive a patent covering a similar field of EPO use. Amgen started legal proceedings against Genetics Institute Inc. and at the time this book was written, the two companies had not reached a settlement.

Biogen's Strategy: A Role Model?

The biotechnology industry displays amazing powers of recovery from hardship and seems to be little affected by temporary setbacks. It always comes up with new ideas and new strategies. The youth of biotechnology companies is their main asset. Because they are so flexible, they can afford to switch strategies overnight and are able to make a fresh start. My last example concerns a company that illustrates this point well: Biogen. Biogen has made a dramatic comeback and has become a favourite again among stock market speculators.

Biogen had its moment of glory with interferon, a natural protein that was originally announced at the end of the 1970s as a miracle anti-cancer drug – which it turned out not to be. By 1985 Biogen was in bad shape. Nobel Prize-winner Walter Gilbert, the famous Harvard professor turned company chief executive officer, left his position abruptly. To bring the company back to its feet, Biogen hired James Vincent, who took drastic measures: cutting expenses; focusing on a limited number of projects, relating to AIDS, cancer and arthritis; closing Swiss and Belgian research laboratories; shutting down Biogen's Swiss production facility; and starting to convert the biotechnology company into a drug-manufacturing company.

As of now, Biogen has developed both a vaccine and a diagnostic test for hepatitis B. It produces alpha-interferon, a genetically engineered drug used in the treatment of venereal warts and Kaposi sarcoma (one of the early clinical manifestations of AIDS) and whose field of application might soon be extended to colon cancer and what is referred to as non-A, non-B chronic hepatitis. Biogen's efforts have paid off and its recovery resulted in a return of $30 million in 1988. For the first time, the company even reported a profit at the beginning of 1989. While biotechnology stocks have remained at their lowest values, Biogen's price went up from $8 to $16 in six months. The capabilities of the company's managers seem perfectly tailored to the needs of a biotechnology company undergoing its metamorphosis into a drug-manufacturing firm. Rumour has it that the staff's morale is at its highest; a sure sign is that employee turnover has shrunk to a minimum – something that all biotechnology companies dream of!

Biogen's current hopes rest on CD-4, a very promising anti-AIDS drug. Its development into a marketable product will take at least another two years. But the company's management is so keen to obtain FDA approval in record time that it is ready to make a new stock offering in order to raise the $50 million necessary to build a CD-4-production facility, as well as to implement an extended sales network. Yet CD-4 may have rough times ahead, due to both its price and competition from other players. The yearly CD-4 treatment cost will be $20,000 per patient. Here again, who will be able to afford it? To what extent will insurance companies reimburse the costs for such a still controversial disease? Furthermore, Genentech and Hoffman-La Roche are currently testing modified CD-4 molecules with a longer-lasting effect of two weeks, compared to one day for the current CD-4 molecule.

These complications have left certain observers with doubts about Biogen's financial future. Some have even said that the company is in a position similar to Amgen's two years ago – a good prospect that did not come to fruition – but I very much doubt it. After all, Biogen has already made a profit – what an auspicious achievement!

Where Is the Original, Humanitarian Goal of Research?

All the considerations discussed in this chapter about the biotechnology companies seem very distant from the original aims of revolutionary drugs as powerful means of fighting disease and of alleviating human suffering. Concepts such as an individual's health and well-being seem to have been lost somewhere along the road. In fact, in all my dealings with biotechnology and pharmaceutical companies over the years I have always had the uneasy feeling that the potential of a drug to treat human disease is a fortuitous side effect, a marketable commodity that helps to win over media attention while the primary goal concerns two of the strongest human motivating factors: greed and ambition. I vividly remember a remark made by a start-up biotechnology company's chief executive: 'This is not the Salvation Army. We have to think of ourselves first. We cannot afford to be guided by humanitarian feelings.' Hard words, but to me they sum up the rules of the game.

Yet however unpalatable the reality may be, we have to accept it and learn how to live with it. It is true that biotechnology holds great promise for the future of mankind. Its tangible products ultimately serve the individual's welfare. But we have to recognize too that biotechnology is an industry, and that the billions of dollars invested are contributing to the making of more powerful and more efficient therapeutic agents. In essence, biotechnology serves the interests of the patient, the investor and the manufacturer. Let us not forget that one person alone can belong to all three groups at the same time.

While looking at biotechnology as an industry, we obviously run into questions of morals, ethics and legality. It is these sensitive points I will consider in the last chapter of this book.

17

The Ethics of Genetics

THE APPLICATIONS OF THE ADVANCES OF BIOTECHNOLOGY IN MEDICINE, and more specifically the large-scale introduction of both genetic testing and genetic screening in the marketplace, stand at the heart of controversies that rage still. We are confronted with disturbing questions whose implications stir our deepest feelings. We have gone beyond the stage of considerations about life and death, for we now have the power to modify the course of natural evolution and thereby the very essence of what humanity really is. Moral, ethical and legal issues pertaining to new genetics are raised at a crucial time when major ideological changes are taking place all over the world and when ethics is taking the lead over logic. There are several reasons for the current changes in the attitudes of society and its growing concern over the validity of existing technologies.

Western cultures see life as a struggle between humans and Nature. This view leaves no alternative but for one side to impose its domination over the other. Of course, there has never been any doubt that the human race would win the battle — an attitude strengthened by Judaeo-Christian traditions. As a consequence, human beings have focused their creativity on the development of technologies of ever-increasing sophistication to tame the natural elements.

Conscience in History

The advent of technological progress as we know it stems from our deterministic conceptualization of our environment in which the universe is viewed as a giant system ruled by laws having cause and effect relationships. Within this system, human beings are nothing but bits of organized physical matter which have developed the extraordinary ability to think. This particularity is at the heart of two major effects. On one hand, thought processes allow us to conceptualize and formulate the laws of physics that govern the universe. On the other hand, our actions are influenced by a fundamental characteristic, subjectivity, which prevents us from yielding exclusively to logic.

With subjective analysis, we reframe the value of our actions and believe in abstract concepts that have no irrefutable proof (we need faith to assume their existence). Subjective analysis is under the control of conscience, which, according to the definition provided by the philosopher Henri Bergson, is a bridge between the past and the future. We use our experience (the fields of probability of the past) to make conscious decisions affecting our future. Conscience dictates the boundaries between good and bad. All human cultures have developed a code of ethics to define a set of actions to be followed in order to perform what is considered to be good and avoid what is felt to be bad.

Value judgements teach us what we should and should not do in order to reach a supreme goal. Philosophers of all times have identified this ultimate goal as a higher value necessary to achieve individual peace of mind. For Aristotle and Epicurus, it was happiness; for Descartes, the incarnation of generosity; for Kant, a symbiosis between virtue and happiness.

Decadence of the Occident

Our perception, conceptualization and definition of objects, phenomena and abstract concepts fluctuate between two opposite frames of mind: rationality and intuition (also referred to as 'reason and heart', 'Einstein and Benares'* and Pascal's *'esprit de géométrie et esprit de finesse'*). Different cultures have put more or less emphasis on one or other of the two at different periods of history. For example, although the ancient Greeks and Romans considered rational ways of thinking very important, they believed in the intervention of magic and consulted with oracles and fortunetellers before making major decisions. Then, while the eighteenth century saw great advances in mathematical thinking, the nineteenth century, the century of technical revolution, adopted a romantic attitude and valued intuition over rational analysis.

Several schools of thought went so far as to suggest that scientists should identify with, rather than dissect or remain outside observers of, their subjects of study. Goethe advocated that scientists should

---

* Benares, now called Varanasi, in India, is the Hindus' holy city.

analyse the studied objects from within. Nietzsche claimed that the objectivity of scientists, as well as their intangible faith in their perception of reality, became the symptom of a decreased vitality, foretelling the decadence of society. This theme was further developed by Oswald Spengler, who in 1920 wrote that the split between the activities of a scientific and intellectual élite and those of the remainder of the population constituted an unmistakable sign of the decadence of the Occident. Spengler's views have been criticized, especially because Nazism took inspiration from some of them, yet we can draw positive messages from his work as a scientific historian and philosopher, in particular in managing its implications. We must not stop thinking about social and cultural responsibilities of science and scientists.

Changes of the 1990s

In 1991, after a frantic race towards technological advances, the pendulum is swinging back from a purely logical view and moral issues are playing a growing role. They will continue to do so over the next decade, and this will instigate new ideological and geopolitical balances. In particular, the trend towards greater uniformity in a nation's way of thinking is spreading throughout the world, and this reinforces the unity among nations. The superpowers are reducing their direct political influence, withdrawing from their role as referees for other countries and concentrating on their own backyards: the USSR has its provinces, the US its poor. Of course, major confrontations will continue to take place here and there, warranting the involvement of advanced nations, whether on humanitarian, ideological or economical grounds. The Gulf War and its consequences have constituted a particularly representative and dramatic episode where coalition forces, in light of a potentially explosive situation, restrained their participation to their original commitment. Over the past two years, the foundations of Communism have been severely shaken. And yet the world is a closed, polycultural system and a change in one part triggers a change somewhere else – a loss is replaced with a gain. Softening ideological and political conflicts are being replaced with religious conflicts – a hallmark of the intuitive and subjective mind.

The next decade will be one of generosity. It has become common to hear that intolerance is intolerable. Public opinion is becoming sensitive to injustice and suffering, whether caused by natural catastrophes or humans. The level of consciousness is rising in situations involving chaos, starvation and racial, cultural and ethnic segregation.

Ecology is another preoccupation. The term is no longer the monopoly of small activist groups considered as marginals by the remainder of society. What we are talking about is no longer an ecology stamped with post-hippie labels but an ecology on a planetary scale aimed at implementing concrete measures that can be reasonably undertaken to stop and set back the damage inflicted by the human race.

Given the connotations of the word 'ecology', maybe we should find another name to refer to a general concern delineating the place of human beings within the universal ecosystem, so that everyone feels part of the outcome of the battle for survival of the planet earth. We have gone too far to stop the engines and return to where we were years ago, but we need to reach a balance to stop the rot.

Protection of animal species nearing extinction, rescue of the Amazonian rainforest and control of the ocean fish depletion are a few examples of situations in which massive information campaigns are starting to pay off.

The 1980s saw a quest for individual success at all costs; the 1990s will raise concerns of a moral and ethical nature on the personal and society levels. More than before, the validity of technical advances is being seriously questioned. Genethics, which proposes to address and regulate the applications of new genetics, came about as a result of these types of worries.

Genetic Testing, Disease Prevention and Respect for the Individual

The efforts of molecular geneticists to map the human genome allow the identification of genes whose abnormalities result in genetic diseases. At the same time, we are also starting to define and quantify vague concepts such as genetic susceptibility to infectious diseases, as well as to multifactorial entities such as character traits, personality traits, IQ, heart disease, hypertension, cancer and mental illnesses. We hope that one day we will be able to characterize all the biochemical functions of the body.

The direct, practical application of the line of studies centred around genome projects is genetic testing. Genetic tests allow us to make accurate diagnoses of specific susceptibilities to complex disorders such as cardiovascular disease; they also constitute, in the form of DNA fingerprints, infallible methods of individual identification. To perform a genetic test, all that is needed is a minute amount of DNA, which can be isolated from any part of the body. Since DNA is available from the time of fecundation, these tests can be done prenatally; with the current methods for obtaining foetal tissue, prenatal diagnoses can be made as early as the sixth week of pregnancy.

The development of genetic tests is the first step towards the ultimate, long-term goal of medical researchers – treatment, cure and eradication of severely debilitating and lethal diseases. The bright side of genetic testing is that the dream of practising true preventive medicine is becoming a reality. The dark side, however, is that these technologies could be used against the will of the individual. The general feeling in scientific and medical communities is that we should not try to stop, or even to slow down, any research whose goal is to treat or cure human disease. On the other hand, to think that science holds the truth on this matter is the first step towards a new form of eugenics.

The impact of biotechnology is identical to that of any other new technological field. Its possibilities have generated a split between admiration for its promise and fear of opening another Pandora's Box. We lack the perspective necessary to analyse patiently the full breadth of the subject. The elaboration of a set of rules for governing the implementation and the use of genetic testing is a formidable task. Deeply rooted emotional issues have raised extreme confusion among and between scientists, physicians, religious groups, lawyers, politicians, moralists and philosophers, both liberal and conservative.

Despite growing concern from all involved parties, we seem to have reached deadlock. The only definite, official statements have been vague and abstract; they have remained at the general level of 'we should be careful to respect human dignity' and the like. Nobody wants to be held responsible for suggesting concrete measures and recommendations.

Researchers have been the first to take this problem seriously. Since the Asilomar conference in 1975, they have not ceased to evaluate the scope of their work. Although scientists are usually perceived as laconic and prudent in their declarations, they have, in evaluating the ramifications of their research, taken the lead. Even though over the years associations such as the American Society of Human Genetics have refused to take political stands, several of its members who disagreed with this attitude have taken positions as individuals.

What is new and troubling about genetic analysis is that it invades all areas of an individual's integrity and privacy: conception, decisions about life and death, health and disease, immigration and selection in the workplace or by insurance companies are the direct implications. It is bringing new means of uncovering an individual's deepest and darkest secrets, unknown even to himself or herself. We are no longer talking about what a person can do, but about who and what this person really is.

Several questions have surfaced over the past few years. Who will perform the tests? How are they going to be used (or misused)? What happens to the results of the tests? Who will have access to them? Who will guarantee their confidentiality? Who should decide whether or not a person gets a test – doctors, employers, insurance companies, government members? On the other hand, do they have a duty to make them available in order to respect the employee's rights to obtain that information?

All these issues beg further emotionally and morally loaded questions. The difficulty of resolving these issues is exacerbated by a paradox involving time: although it is too early to assess a subject which is open-ended, several tests have already reached the marketplace and are routinely performed. And these constitute only a small portion of the 3,500 or so genetic diseases making up the morbid panoply. The number of genetic tests for these diseases, however, increases every day.

Yet there are no general regulations governing the use of these tests. We are facing a formidable workload, because each of these tests will raise slightly different questions. Meanwhile, genetic diseases remain untreatable: the development of appropriate treatment modalities is slower in coming than the development of diagnostic tests. Today, the existence of a genetic test for a disease when no treatment is available has only painful consequences, including abortion of affected foetuses and denial of both insurance policies and employment to affected adults. No wonder, then, that objections have been put forward. Indeed, what kind of life lies ahead of an individual who learns that he or she is the carrier of a severe genetic illness?

Rights to Abortion: What Limits?

Huntington's disease (HD) represents an example of this situation, and it illustrates many of the concerns raised by early detection of genetic diseases. HD is an autosomal dominant disease: that is, only one abnormal chromosome inherited from one parent causes the illness. It manifests itself at about forty years of age and progresses as a slow degeneracy of the nervous system. Several years of physical and mental impairment lead to a sure death. Although nothing can be done to modify the unavoidable progression of the disease, affected individuals can be identified with DNA tests, which allow doctors to diagnose the disease at any time (prenatally, in childhood, in early adulthood), and that means before the first symptoms appear. Under these conditions, it is therefore possible to warn potential sufferers of a disease usually seen as a death sentence.

Besides, even the results of a prenatal test can give clues about the status of the parents. Let us take the example of a mother who belongs to a family at high risk of HD. She wants to know whether her foetus is affected, but she does not want to know about herself. If the test is positive – that is, the foetus is found to be a carrier of the HD gene – it means that the mother is also a carrier and that she will die from the consequences of HD. On the other hand, if the test is negative, there is still a 50 per cent chance that she is a carrier, and upon hearing why she has requested prenatal testing, people in her environment – and particularly her employers – might change their attitude; she might be looked at as 'probably abnormal'.

Then, unless we want to implement a massive campaign aimed at decreasing and eventually eradicating the HD trait, what right do we have to decide to abort a foetus carrying HD? True, this person, in our current state of medical knowledge, will die by the age of forty, and until the preliminary symptoms appear, maybe in the late thirties, he or she will live a 'normal' life. It is just that the life span is shortened. To my mind there are three reasons for opposing abortion of the affected foetus in such a case. First, a genius like Mozart died at thirty-five. Second, the HD carrier might be killed at twenty-five in a car crash. And third, we tend to forget that biomedical advances can yield treatments of the disease. Of course, it is easy for me to offer rational explanations on the subject because I am not an HD carrier and also because I do not personally know anybody suffering from HD. Someone with the emotional burden of the disease might feel differently.

Who Is Normal?

The boundaries between definitions of a morbid or a lethal trait and an 'abnormal' trait are not only fuzzy; they are also constantly moving. They depend on the culture and on the ethnic group under consideration. But even within a given ethnic group, there is a lack of agreement on what 'ideal' and 'normal' traits should be. Should we seek to eliminate genetic disease? If so, what level of severity should constitute the cut-off point? Should we prevent individuals considered as unfit by a given society from having children? By what means? If we were to eliminate the schizophrenia trait, for example, many investigators claim that creativity in the liberal arts would also disappear (this assertion is the subject of debate, but it has not been categorically refuted).

The very idea of selecting for desired traits is not only theoretically impossible, because of DNA mutation and recombination events; it is also absurd. Where would we stop? Any physical and behavioural trait can become a subject of disagreement. Some members of our society would certainly want to go for blue-eyed, blond-haired types – there is a historical precedent for that. And what about our conception of intelligence? Should we seek to raise systematically all IQs? The mean value in the population would still be 100. How about height? Researchers working on projects implicated in the study of human growth hormone (GH) have been surprised by the numbers of parents who come and see them. And I am not talking about parents whose children are affected with dwarfism, which can be treated with GH, but about parents who have normal kids with respect to height and who wish them to become 'tall' kids, despite the horrendous cost of several tens of thousands of dollars and also despite the recognized side effects associated with hormonal imbalances. Then again, what can possibly be an ideal height? If everybody was 7 feet high, those who wanted to feel taller would have to go for 8 feet.

Along the same lines, why not take into consideration the size of certain external organs? This would certainly introduce an even stronger bias towards assortative mating.

We have to accept that people are not created equal. As all other living species, they show a remarkable diversity – a continuous spectrum of different physical and behavioural traits. This wide spectrum is due to the presence of genetic polymorphisms, which form the basis for evolution and the essence of living organisms. Genetic variability also confers characteristics that can adapt to changes in the environment. Adaptation is intimately associated with the concept of survival of the fittest and is entirely responsible for the fact that we humans exist. If we were to restrict the frame of these variations to an extreme degree, we would tend towards uniformity and dullness, towards the engineering of robot-like creatures.

Both the idea of moulding humans according to predetermined quality criteria and the means of doing so have been put into application in several instances. The list of a few precedents – including the Nazi experience, sterility campaigns for the 'mentally abnormal', choice of children's gender (male in 98 per cent of cases), storage of sperm from Nobel Prize recipients as a marketable commodity – remind us that these situations have led to bitter objections at best and atrocities at worst.

Money, Patents and Business

The dichotomy between what is theoretically possible and the concrete applications of biotechnology is due to the scale of the funds and the effort involved. Scientific investigation in general is expensive, but the budget of biotechnology is such that this field ranks with space programmes, supraconductivity and subatomic particle physics. Moreover, basic research is only the preliminary stage in the introduction of practical applications on the market. The cost of validation of genetic tests has slowed down the pace of Research and Development.

Yet the incentive for biotechnology companies to invest sizeable sums of money lies in the putative commercial rewards. Marketing departments in pharmaceutical and biotechnology companies have long been impressed with the market size. Indeed, every human being is a potential candidate for some genetic tests. Although analysts have traditionally made prudent forecasts and although no one can predict the extent of application of these tests over the next decades, specialists do not hesitate to quote annual market figures ranging from hundreds of millions to billions of dollars.

To make sure that they do not miss out on any opportunity, companies and universities alike have engaged in a frantic race for patents. Investigators involved in the field of biotechnology are pressured to file patent applications on results that seem to be of potential value. Lawyers are swamped with new applications and it is impossible at this time to guess what is patentable and what is not. The two most common side effects of this frenzied situation are, first, a precipitate introduction of these technologies into the public domain – as was the case for the use of DNA fingerprints as forensic tools – and, second, bitter legal battles between companies. Greed for money (and fame) has reached the benches of research laboratories, exacerbating tensions between research groups to the point where sharp practice in disciplines which claim to be rigorous and unselfish are becoming commonplace. The race to report genetic markers associated with the gene responsible for cystic fibrosis (located on chromosome 7), for example, has led to ridiculous and questionable ways of proceeding on the part of several research teams.

In the scientific community, it has been implicit (although unofficial) for a long time now that the human genome cannot be patented; no one could claim rights on it. What is patentable, however, is a demonstrated association between a genetic marker (or a set of genetic markers) and the clinical manifestation of a given disease.

Before reaching the marketplace, a diagnostic test needs to be approved by the FDA, which requests information on the sensitivity and the specificity of the test procedure. The sensitivity is the probability that the test is positive in a person affected by the disease; specificity is the probability that the test is positive in a person who is disease-free. For two main reasons (genetic heterogeneity of diseased conditions and the fact that linked genetic markers form the basis for most genetic tests), both false positives and false negatives are unavoidable. The FDA thus needs to define acceptable levels of sensitivity and specificity. As of now, a laboratory providing genetic testing services using DNA tests developed in its own research laboratories does not need FDA approval. This is why, at the moment, the main objective of professionals involved in genetic testing is the definition of standards for good laboratory practice. DNA tests still represent sophisticated procedures requiring highly trained personnel. Automation of these procedures will improve both the reproducibility of the tests and the quality control. Besides, an increasing number of laboratories will also be able to include genetic testing in their battery of tests. Wide and uncontrolled proliferation of genetic screening centres, however, is undesirable at this point.

Indeed, the spread of genetic-testing laboratories is a source of worry since there is an imbalance between the availability of genetic tests and the number of professionals required to handle all aspects of these tests. Genetics is still a neglected discipline, even in medical schools. Yet the health care system will need to undergo major reorganization in order to accommodate the widespread introduction of genetic testing. There is an urgent need to increase scientific literacy and, in particular, the concepts of molecular genetics among doctors, nurses, social workers, laboratory technicians, as well as the general public. Many scientists have advocated that, in the beginning anyway, the right to provide genetic testing should be restricted to specific reference centres set up with qualified personnel and the necessary structure for offering psychological support to individuals who have to suffer the trauma of hearing undesired results of tests.

Wide dissemination of information is of the utmost importance if we want to be able to make sound decisions about the elaboration of accepted laws for governing the implications of new genetics. Everyone should clearly understand all possible ramifications, so as to avoid violent, unconditional reactions of the type taking place in Germany, where activist groups are pushing the government to block research and the application of genetic engineering.

That people, in Germany as in other countries, are reluctant to accept the release of genetically engineered organisms in the environment is understandable. We have already witnessed the proliferation of transgenic plants: that is, plants in which scientists have introduced foreign genes to confer specific characteristics – prevention of freezing in strawberries; herbicide resistance in tomatoes, soya beans, cotton or root beets; and virus and insect resistance in tobacco plants. The fear remains that transgenic plants could transmit their foreign gene characteristics to other hosts and affect ecosystems in an unthought-of fashion.

In Germany, however, worries about genetic manipulations are more deeply rooted in the individual's mind. In 1987, John Baxter, the manager of California Biotechnology's marketing department, and I went to Germany to start negotiations with the management team of a giant pharmaceutical company, which was keenly interested in the development of genetic tests for predicting an individual's susceptibility to heart disease. Their long-term plan was to introduce DNA testing to their range of diagnostic tests and become Europe's leader in that field. The meetings went well and everyone was pleased with the outcome.

We went to dinner in a charming little countryside village. On the way back to the hotel, I was in the same taxi as a famous German professor of human genetics who had been asked by the pharmaceutical company to be a consultant and adviser on this particular deal. After a few minutes of social chat, he looked concerned and embarked on what was really puzzling him. 'You know,' he said, 'the DNA tests you are working on are extremely interesting and undoubtedly of great value in the medical field. I am all for that type of research. However, we Germans have to be very careful with it. Otherwise, people in the rest of the world will say: "Oh, no! They are doing it again!" '

In the end, that particular company did not sign an agreement with us – not, however, entirely for ethical reasons but because the results we presented to them were too preliminary.

The Stories of Steve and Mike

At its profoundest, new genetics could generate a blueprint for a new type of society. At the same time, genetic testing forces us to reconsider an individual's rights as opposed to those of an employer or an insurer. The introduction of genetic testing in the workplace raises sensitive questions because, in the present state of knowledge, test results can lead only to job denial. Let us take two examples.

Steve was born and raised in a small Midwestern town where

his family has always lived. At the age of eighteen, he applies for a job in the only factory of the area – a chemical company. As the other members of his family were, he is certain to get a job there. The personnel officer requests a genetic profile, which reveals a high susceptibility to the types of chemicals manufactured in the town's company. His job application is turned down.

Now in his forties, Mike has climbed the ladder of corporate hierarchy and is being considered for the position of vice-president of the business department. Results of his genetic analysis, however, indicate that he is at a higher than average risk of suffering a premature heart attack. Chances are that the hiring committee will want to take on someone else for that position.

Genetic Discrimination

Some genetic defects are more prevalent in some particular ethnic groups (the higher incidence of sickle cell anaemia among Blacks is the most frequently cited example). Discrimination on the basis of these defects will tend to be subsumed under racial discrimination. In fact, when it turns to genetic disease, each individual becomes a minority member because of his or her particular predisposition to a particular set of medical conditions. The problem is that, until the human genome is completely mapped, there will be no guarantee that the best person has been hired for any job. Besides, current tests can only identify a few deleterious traits in some individuals. In the future, why not anticipate the discovery of genetic traits conferring a predisposition to better job performance?

Genetic tests constitute much-awaited means for insurance companies to control premiums and deny rights to policies. The discrimination exists already and is based on both family and personal medical histories. If every condition becomes foreseeable, however, insurers might need to adjust their rates to every individual. On the other hand, if everybody can get access to genetic analysis, insurance companies will run into adverse selection: that is, it will be mostly individuals at higher risk who seek to obtain extensive health and life cover.

We Need to Conserve Precious Hereditary Make-ups

Genetic therapy represents another controversial subject. We need to make a clear distinction between therapies done in germ cells (where the DNA modification is transmitted to the offspring) and those done in somatic (non-sexual) cells. Gene therapy in germ cells (or in the egg or the embryo) has been referred to by several scientists as an elegant and efficient way to eradicate a large number of hereditary diseases for which there is no treatment, or when the abnormal cells are accessible with difficulty. At the moment, however, DNA manipulation in germ cells is banned: the human genome cannot be modified in a permanent manner.

As for somatic-cell gene therapy, many investigators argue that there is no fundamental difference between this and an organ graft, which consists of introducing into an organism the cells (with their genetic material) of a donor; in this respect, organ graft amounts to introducing foreign DNA into an organism – precisely the main reproach of detractors of genetic manipulation.

Babies 'à la Carte'

The growing role of *in vitro* fertilization will make it even more difficult to resist the temptation of engineering transmissible DNA modifications. *In vitro* fertilization, or fertilization outside the organism, is the revolutionary method to fight couple sterility (Louise Brown, the first 'test tube baby', was born in July 1978). In this method, several ova are fertilized in the laboratory, although only one egg is necessary. What do we do with the other eggs? A possibility that might be accepted in the future is to grow and check one egg for DNA abnormality, while another one is kept aside for implantation if the results of the genetic analysis should prove satisfactory.

We need to be aware, however, that the temptation will remain, once adequate technologies make it feasible, to modify at will certain genetic characteristics of the egg to be implanted and to manufacture babies 'à la carte'.

Use of Our Knowledge

In the evaluations of the implications of new genetics, we need to make a clear distinction between two concepts: the acquisition of knowledge and the use of this knowledge. Nobody can stop the acquisition of knowledge, and legitimate fears raised about its application should not prevent current research efforts. Introduction of the methods in the marketplace, however, will have to be strictly controlled.

Conclusion

THE RAMIFICATIONS OF THE METHODOLOGY OF MOLECULAR GENETICS extend well beyond the introduction of new techniques into medical practice. By manipulating the genetic material, we touch upon the very essence of life. We can modify in an instant the life resulting from 4.5 billion years of evolution. Do we have the right to modify what certain people call Nature's legacy and others, God's work?

These are indeed very disturbing questions. They may ultimately have to be resolved by appropriate legislation. It is everybody's responsibility to face these issues. We all have the duty to voice our concerns and also to offer suggestions as to the way to handle these controversial arguments.

Learning to Control our Powers

In 1963 Jean Fourastié published a book entitled 'Le Grand Espoir du XXe siècle', in which he wrote:

> One of the causes of the present-day misfortunes of mankind is the fact that the economic and social sciences lag behind the physical sciences. Man is swept along by technical progress towards undreamt of horizons. In the place he occupies between a past that seems thoroughly outmoded and a future that is unknown, Man has none of the traditions, moral values and religious beliefs that once made him a balanced individual, both mentally and socially . . . He has lost all sense of proportion as to what is possible and what is impossible . . .

These words are timeless: they apply equally well today. Wouldn't it be an accomplishment, though, if for once we felt in a position to control the consequences of our technical progress, rather than being swept along by them? It is what molecular biologists are trying to do, maybe for the very first time. Then again, the main value of history is to be able to learn from it.

Genetic Diversity

Diversity is what rules the world. Genetic diversity as we observe it today is the legacy of 4.5 billion years of evolution. It must command respect on the part of humans who are only the latest species to appear on the surface of the earth. To respect the remainder of the universe, we must first learn to accept our own genetic diversity.

True, we all carry deleterious traits, and in particular genes that predispose us to various diseases. We pass these on to our offspring. Given the outcome of the lottery of life, our children might be fine or they might suffer from terrible diseases; they can be bright or they can be mentally retarded; they can be kind or they can be unpleasant.

At this time, we have the chance to formulate guidelines for regulating the use of our powers to manipulate genetic make-ups. We need to keep in mind that we have discovered only the shore of a vast ocean; it will take decades or even centuries to cross the water. Considering that our state of knowledge allows us to provide educated advice about diseases that we understand well, we need to take appropriate decisions in all good faith and with modesty. Let us not believe blindly in science alone, because we do not yet have the key of the lottery of life.

We have to start accepting ourselves as we are — and that may be the most difficult task of all. What right do we have to demand that our children be perfect while we know that we are not? Before engaging in heated debates about the future of humankind, we need to realize and to admit that *we* are not perfect. After all, isn't that to be human?

Index